CLAUDIUS COULIN

STEP-BY-STEP PERSPECTIVE DRAWING

FOR ARCHITECTS, DRAFTSMEN, AND DESIGNERS

TRANSLATED BY JOHN H. YARBROUGH

VAN NOSTRAND REINHOLD COMPANY
NEW YORK CINCINNATI TORONTO LONDON MELBOURNE

Van Nostrand Reinhold Company Regional Offices:
New York Cincinnati Chicago Millbrae Dallas

Van Nostrand Reinhold Company International Offices:
London Toronto Melbourne

German edition, *Zeichenlehre für Architekten,
Bauzeichner und Designer,* © 1966 by
Julius Hoffmann, Stuttgart

Library of Congress Catalog Card No. 67-24692

Published in the United States of America by
Van Nostrand Reinhold Company,
A Division of Litton Educational Publishing, Inc.,
450 West 33rd Street, New York, N.Y. 10001

Published simultaneously in Canada by
Van Nostrand Reinhold Company Ltd.

16 15 14 13 12 11 10 9 8 7 6 5 4 3 2 1

A generation ago the architect usually began his career as a combination janitor and office boy. As a professional his first job was as an eraser. After a drawing had been inked in he was required to remove any leftover pencil lines or smudges with an eraser. He was carefully supervised in this, as he was in each subsequent step of the way—finally mastering his craft after he had progressed through his apprenticeship. Did this mastery of fundamentals ultimately make him a better architect? Would Beethoven's symphonies have been as superb if the composer had not known how to read and write music? I suppose we really do not know.

These days most people seem to prefer to be machine tenders rather than active participants in any particular process. Nevertheless there are still people who believe in mastering the fundamentals of architectural drawing. This book, first published in Germany in 1966, is clearly for them. It will be appreciated also by anyone—architect, artist, engineer, industrial designer—who wishes to expand his spatial and geometrical thinking. The material is organized by degree of complexity, and the principles behind each technical drawing are explained, so that anyone wishing to learn can teach himself.

The book has been painstakingly translated. Few editorial changes have been made in the text, because it seemed wisest to let the author speak for himself as nearly as that is possible in a translation. This also required that none of the drawings or text be deleted. A very brief discussion of color in drawing was deleted, however, along with an illustration of a color-action polygon. This material is irrelevant in American practice because color is not used in working drawings. The author did, however, refer to several books on color, which he considers standard. They are:

F. Birren, *Color, Form and Space* (New York: Van Nostrand Reinhold, 1961)

H. Frieling, *Praktische Farbenlehre,* Lehrmeister-Bücherei No. 1316 (Minden, Germany: A. Philler, 1956)

J. Itten, *Kunst der Farbe* (Ravensburg, Germany: Otto Maier, 1961); published in the United States as *The Elements of Color* (New York: Van Nostrand Reinhold, 1970).

H. Ketcham, *Color Planning* (New York: Harper & Row, 1958)

Otherwise, in places where American and European practice differ or where the text may seem ambiguous, annotations have been added. They appear with the text but within brackets. Any reader who takes the time to make his own original drawing of each of Claudius Coulin's plates not only will increase his understanding of geometry but will be able to construct accurate perspectives from the most complicated and elaborate plans and elevations.

Contents

Building, together with all of its related fields, is one of the most important human endeavors. Architects and builders have always played a definite role in the cultural and social achievements of their time. In our modern industrial society, their problems have been both multiplied and enlarged to an extent never expected. Those engaged in the planning and execution of building projects specialize more and more in particular areas and have unlimited possibilities for training in their respective fields. But all who take part in the realization of a building project have one thing in common—they must be able to draw and to work from a drawing.

This drawing manual answers the question "How is a technical drawing for the building trade carried out?" Beginning with a general terminology of drawing instruments and their use, the entire knowledge necessary for the completion of an architectural drawing is covered. Each drawing illustrates a three-dimensional object on one plane—the drawing surface. The drawing of all forms used in the art and science of building, either individually or coupled with other forms, is thoroughly explored.

The material is organized according to the degree of complexity of construction and is covered to the extent that each technical drawing or geometrical problem is at least explained in principle.

This organization makes it possible for those who are interested to teach themselves technical drawing or to supplement their present knowledge. For self-teaching, it is recommended that all construction be drawn to twice the given scale. If great attention is given to accuracy, this can be good technical drawing practice, and, if the construction is difficult, the exercise will act as a test of how well you have mastered the problem.

For the practicing architect, this manual is a concentrated, clear review and a practical aid in the drawing of difficult details or certain perspectives. For the free-lance artist, or anyone else interested in drawing, this manual provides a complete survey of spatial thinking and geometrical-technical drawing for architects, making it possible, therefore, for one to make correct technical drawings in the solution of common drafting problems.

C. Coulin

Photographs
Page 17: Pyramids of Giza, aerial photo. **Page 49:** Office Building in Salisbury, Southern Rhodesia, architects W. D'Arcy Cathcart and Son, Creasy and Fothergill, Dennis Lennon, Salisbury, from " 'ac' Internationale Asbestcementrevue" (Switzerland, February 1964). **Page 50:** Erich Mendelsohn, idea sketch for the Einstein Tower, Potsdam, 1920, from Erich Mendelsohn, "Das Gesamtschaffen des Architekten" (Rudolf Mosse, Berlin, 1930). **Page 51:** Theater in the Gendarmenmarkt, Berlin, pen and sepia drawing by Schinkel, 1820, photograph, 1935 (Staatliche Bildstelle, Berlin), both from P. O. Rave, "Schinkel—Berlin" (Deutscher Kunstverlag, Berlin, 1941); Helmut Jacoby, office building in Baltimore, 1961, architect Ludwig Mies van der Rohe, from C. Coulin, "Architekten zeichnen," (Julius Hoffmann, Stuttgart, 1962). **Page 77:** R. Buckminster Fuller, Double Shell Dome in Cleveland, Ohio, 1959, from R. W. Marks, "The Dymaxion World of Buckminster Fuller" (Van Nostrand Reinhold, New York, 1960). **Page 79:** Stairway in an administration building, architects D. Badani, A. Kandijan, P. Roux-Dorlut and M. Folliason, Paris, from F. Schuster, "Treppen" (Julius Hoffmann, Stuttgart, 1964); chapel for the Air Force Academy, Colorado Springs, Architects Skidmore, Owings and Merrill, New York, photo Stewarts, Colorado Springs; tent for the National Garden Show, Cologne, 1957, architects Frei Otto, Siegfried Lohs, Ewald Bubner, and Diether R. Frank.

Introduction: Materials and Techniques

Paper

Drawings are made on paper. Although one can draw on almost any type of paper, not every kind is suitable for a good technical drawing. Before making a selection, consider the following:

Kind of drawing. A preliminary drawing is usually developed on a heavy paper which will stand up under repeated erasures and changes.

Method of execution. A pencil drawing will require a different type of paper than an ink drawing. Translucent paper will be used if one drawing is to be done over another, for example, an elevation drawing over a corresponding plan.

Type of reproduction. A translucent paper must be used if blueprints or similar contact prints are to be made from the original.

Opaque paper is produced in many different grades. Drawing paper and very heavy paper called "board" come in varying tones of white with either a smooth or rough surface. Treated paper on which ink will not run is also available.

Translucent paper may be bought in different tones of white, in different weights, and in different degrees of translucency.

Special types of drawing media. Some drawing media are not paper but plastic products. They are used for drawings which must be absolutely free of distortions. Some of the special drawing media are mounted drawing paper, tracing cloth, drawing and tracing glass cloth, and drafting film. A non-print grid is available in some media.

Characteristics of papers. As a result of the necessary stages in its production, all paper has a smooth and rough side. Before beginning to draw, one must decide which side is more suitable for a particular drawing. The proper lead or pen point is then selected for the paper chosen. Translucent paper, with the exception of a few special types, is rather sensitive to water. Wet spots on nearly all paper become rough and wavy after drying, thereby making the paper unsuitable for an exact drawing. Translucent paper becomes so wavy that it is unusable. Thus, you must protect drawings from all forms of moisture. Waterproof paper is available, however. All paper "breathes"—that is, it expands and contracts, like lumber, according to its moisture content. Because of this, paper for related drawings is often cut from the same roll. Paper expands and contracts perpendicular to the grain more than it does with the grain. Generally, translucent paper expands and contracts more than opaque paper.

Identification of paper is accomplished by the use of the catalog number, name, color, thickness, rag content, grain, transparency, and any special characteristics (moisture proof, non-print grid, satin finish on both sides, one side dull, the other side coated, etc.). Paper is produced in rolls or sheets of different sizes. If a subject drawing is to be on several sheets, the sheet size selected is determined by the requirements of the largest single drawing. Sheet sizes for architectural drawings are more or less standard. For practical reasons, it is recommended that drawings be made on standard-size sheets. For example, blueprint paper is produced to accommodate the size of translucent sheets.

Cut Sheet Sizes

	Table 1			Table 2	
Desig-nation	Width in inches	Length in inches	Desig-nation	Width in inches	Length in inches
A	8½	11	A	9	12
B	11	17	B	12	18
C	17	22	C	18	24
D	22	34	D	24	36
E	34	44	E	36	48

[**Note:** In the United States the basic drawing is usually executed on detail paper and the final drawing on tracing paper or tracing vellum; paper is usually cut from rolls. The author had included, among special types of drawing media, mounted drawing paper and drawing and tracing glass, but these are of little interest in this country. Two plastic media commonly used are Mylar, made by Du Pont, and Estar, made by Kodak. Most drafting films are one of these generic types with a trade name applied.

In the drawings on page 9, European paper sizes have been changed to U.S. standard sizes. Although tracing-paper pads of these sizes are available, most offices either cut their stock from rolls which are manufactured in various widths and lengths, or employ standard-size sheets with their name pre-printed in one corner.]

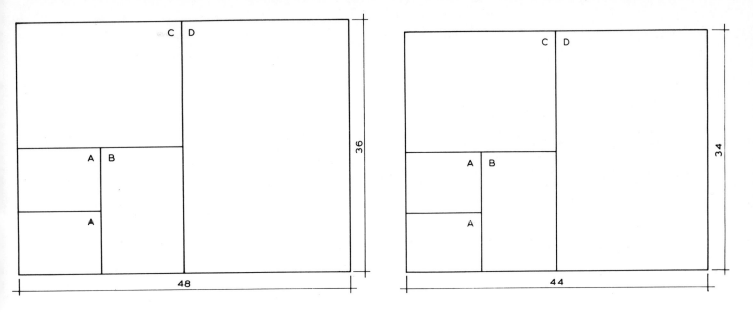

Overall view of ASA paper sizes A to E

By dividing a sheet in half, the next size smaller is obtained.

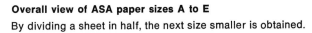

ASA size B with border.

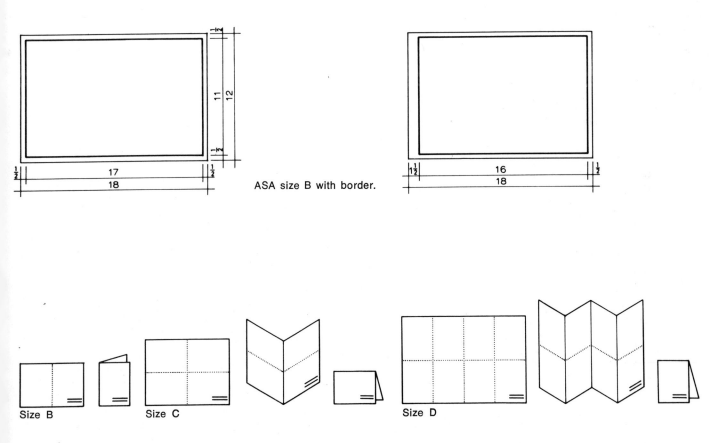

Size B   Size C   Size D

Sheet folding

In folding a sheet, the objective is to obtain a standard size which will fit into a standard file folder or cabinet and to have the title block appear on the top fold.

Drawing instruments

A variety of instruments is needed for drafting. The most common are mentioned here. Excellent brochures on every make of all categories are available; therefore, a detailed description is unnecessary. Also, a visit to one of the better architects' and engineers' supply stores, where you can see the actual tool, is much more interesting than any written description.

The drawing board, or table, should be of knot-free, well-seasoned white pine or basswood. Boards are available in several sizes, corresponding, to some extent, with the sheet sizes of drawing paper. For most student drawing, 24″ × 36″ or 31″ × 42″ is sufficient. However, office requirements will vary. The drawing board should be rectangular and completely flat with all adjacent edges exactly 90° to each other. At least two adjacent edges should be tested before purchasing. These can then be used as the true front edge and the left-hand edge. [**Note:** Unless you contemplate buying a cheap nonprofessional drawing board it is not necessary in the United States to test the edges of a drawing board because they are precisely made. Many draftsmen prefer a board with a built-in straightedge rather than the conventional T-square. This is mounted on a track and is easily moved up and down the board.]

Drafting machines are available in different price ranges, according to their design, precision, and flexibility. The drawing board is usually mounted on an adjustable stand with varying degrees of tilt and sometimes with variable height adjustment. A high-precision drafting machine unites T-square, triangles, scale, and protractor all in one instrument.

Perspective drawing machines. For the construction of perspectives, there are several machines available which make possible a simple and time-saving construction. Such a machine is recommended if perspectives are to be constructed frequently.

Drawing-board cover. In order to make exact drawings, the drawing board must be fitted with a slightly tinted, hard, somewhat resilient material, such as heavy cardboard, linoleum, or plastic. With such a background, lines on translucent paper appear much more clearly, and heavy pencil lines can be drawn without damage to the paper.

Fastening paper. Paper is secured to the drawing board with thumbtacks (for heavy paper) or masking tape (for lightweight paper). Masking tape is used on hard drawing-board covers or hardwood drawing boards, but thumbtacks are more practical if the drawing must be removed often. Heavyweight paper (board) can also be glued to the drawing board. However, the sheet should first be well moistened on both sides (which will cause it to stretch) and then glued to the drawing board all around the border. In drying, the paper contracts and forms a good, even drawing surface.

Drawing pencils, both wood and mechanical, come in various styles and price ranges. Of primary importance in drafting is the quality of the line—its sharpness, uniformity, and density. Drawing-pencil lead designations go from 9H (hard) to 4B and 6B (soft); H, HB, and F are in the medium range.

Color pencils are used in technical drawings for precise colored lines, for crosshatching, or for indicating areas in color. Only good-quality pencils are suitable for this purpose.

Charcoal, pastel crayons. Charcoal pencils are available in different types and degrees of hardness. They are used for design sketches or presentation drawings. Drawings made in charcoal pastel must, however, be sprayed with a fixative in order to prevent smearing. Pastel crayons are used like charcoal, but produce either white or colored drawings. [**Note:** Color is rarely used on working drawings in the United States these days, charcoal and pastels almost never. When color is required, felt pens are usually used.]

Pencil sharpener. The simplest point-making instrument is a sharp pocketknife. With an emery-paper pencil sharpener, one can also sharpen a pencil lead as precisely as desired. There are a number of manual and electric pencil sharpeners on the market, which vary in price and quality. It is, of course, best to try one out before buying it. [**Note:** Most U.S. offices have electric pencil sharpeners.]

The T-square, previously all wood but now primarily made of plastic, is the simplest drawing machine. With it all parallel horizontal lines are drawn. The T-square head must be fixed in an exact perpendicular securely to the blade so that all lines drawn along the blade remain parallel. There are also T-squares with adjustable blades for the drawing of parallel oblique lines.

Triangles. All vertical and diagonal lines are drawn with a triangle. A small triangle works well for designing and for the construction of small isolated drawings. For working drawings, however, it is advisable to choose a triangle large enough to draw the longest lines with one stroke. There are two kinds of non-adjustable triangles: one with angles of 45°, 45° and 90°, the other with angles of 30°, 60° and 90°. Adjustable triangles are also available with which one can draw a line at any degree to the horizontal.

The scale rule. The most common scale rule is flat with a 12-inch scale in 1/16″ divisions on one edge and 1/8″ and 1/4″ divisions on the other. The triangular architectural scale shows, on the side most frequently used, 1/8″ = 1′0″ and 1/4″ = 1′0″ on one edge, and 1/2″ = 1′0″ and 1″ = 1′0″ on the opposite edge. A second side shows 1/16″ divisions on one edge, and 3/16″ = 1′0″ and 3/32″ = 1′0″ on the opposite edge. The third side shows 3/8″ = 1′0″ and 3/4″ = 1′0″ on one edge, and 1 1/2″ = 1′0″ and 3″ = 1′0″ on the opposite edge. The first side is used for most working drawings; the second side is primarily used for small-scale drawings; and the third side is generally used for detail drawings. The most common scale in the metric system is the 30-centimeter scale with millimeter divisions on one side and half-millimeter divisions on the other. The common triangular scales show 1 : 2.5, 1 : 5, 1 : 10, 1 : 20, 1 : 50, and 1 : 100. There are, however, other combinations.

Protractor. In drafting, all angles are measured in degrees or pitch. For angles other than 30°, 45°, and 60°, a protractor must be used. Some adjustable triangles have the degree readings, others also have the pitch, which is useful in showing a roof pitch. Other angles can be created without the use of a protractor by using two triangles together. [**Note:** The protractor is rarely used in drafting in the United States today.]

Compasses are available from simple circle compasses to various precision instruments. The divider is used to transfer exact measurements from one drawing to another. The drop compass is used to draw extremely small circles. It should be sufficient for the architect to have a good ruling pen, a friction compass, a friction divider, and a bow compass with screw adjustment.

French curves and templates are available in different sizes for drawing circles, ellipses, and other curves. An ellipse curve and a large and small spiral curve are usually sufficient for the needs of architectural draftsmen. A flexible plastic curve also has been proved useful.

Furniture and fixture templates of different kinds, used for quick scale drawing of furniture and fixtures on plans, are also available; they are usually in ¼″ and ⅛″ scale.

Lettering templates, available in alphabets of various size, make it possible to letter neatly and uniformly with pencil or ink. Larger, individual letter templates that can be used with a spray are also available.

Ink is used for drawings on which no important changes are expected to be made. A drawing is made in ink either for better reproduction (contact print, lithograph, or other) or for graphic reasons (competition drawings, presentation drawings). There are several types of ink. In order to achieve a lighter line, one may use drawing ink thinned with distilled water. Drawing ink diluted with ten parts of water to one part of ammonia also gives satisfactory results. [**Note:** Drawing inks are rarely thinned these days.]

Drawing pens are similar to the simple writing pen. They are used for drawing the freehand line and are made in different widths and degrees of flexibility for various types of line and drawing techniques.

The ruling pen is used with the T-square and triangles to draw exact lines. In order to be able to adjust the width of the line accurately, it is recommended that a ruling pen with an adjustment screw with numbered settings be used. Ruling pens for compasses are also available.

Fountain pens, such as Graphos and Rapidograph, relieve the draftsman of constant refilling. Detailed brochures on the various types and their uses may be had from the respective firms or dealers.

Other drawing pens, such as Flo-master, Pentel, etc., have, in general, a drawing point of felt or other similar porous material. They produce a very legible sharp line; its graphic effect approaches that of the pencil. These pens, available in different colors, are used for freehand drawing, lettering, and color sketches on transparent paper.

Water colors. There are basically two types of water color. Traditional water color is transparent; the other type—known as tempera or poster color—is opaque. However, water color may not be used on translucent paper because of the paper's sensitivity to moisture.

Erasers are produced in varying degrees of hardness—from a soft kneaded eraser for charcoal lines to the hard abrasive erasers for ink. The eraser must correspond to the kind of line and the texture of paper being used, and must effectively erase the line without damaging the paper.

Fiber glass erasers, knives, and electric erasers are used to erase ink lines. Electric erasing machines are often also used for pencil drawings.

Eradicator fluid. Pencil lines, especially on tracing paper, can be easily and completely erased with benzene-moistened cotton without damaging either ink lines or the paper. Benzene fumes are poisonous and the chemical must be used with care. [**Note:** Benzene is also highly flammable. Carbon tetrachloride, sold under the trade name Carbona, is nonflammable and can be used instead of benzene, although it too is toxic.] When many changes have to be made on a completed drawing, it is best to make a master print. One can eradicate the unwanted lines on this master print with eradicator fluid (available for different printing processes), and then complete the drawing as desired.

Erasing shields of metal or plastic simplify clean erasures. They segregate the area to be erased to prevent smearing the adjacent parts of the drawing.

Drafting brushes. After erasures, the drawing is swept clean with a soft-bristled cleaning brush, dense enough to remove all small particles.

Atomizers are used to spray fixative on pencil and charcoal drawings to prevent their becoming smeared. They are also used to spray ink or color on a drawing.

Paper cutter and binding. The completed drawings can be reduced to the correct size with a knife, scissors, or paper cutter. As a protection against tearing the edges, a binding—applied by hand or mechanically—is sometimes fixed along the lefthand edge.

Storage, care, and reproduction of drawings. There is a variety of furniture and equipment for these purposes. Since these deal only indirectly with drawing, they need not be discussed.

Drawing Technique

In drawing, as in every handcraft, there are different techniques of execution and work which require experience and practice to master. The production of architectural drawings requires concentration and attention to detail. Working tempo, rhythm, and material produce the character of a drawing. The work table and drawing instruments must be kept clean. The drawing area must be well and correctly lighted. If a drawing remains fastened to the drawing table for an extended period without being worked on, it should be covered with a heavy sheet of drawing board to protect it against dust and moisture.

Drawing in pencil is the quickest and most versatile drawing technique. No other medium offers such variety of line quality and precision. For example, a line starting thin and light, and increasing gradually in width and intensity, can be drawn only in pencil. Ink drawings are drawn first in pencil. Each technical drawing is developed from one or more horizontal and vertical reference lines on which the respective lengths and heights are indicated. From these measuring points other light construction lines are then drawn in the necessary directions; the drawing is thus initially laid out. The construction lines and their intersections produce a plan of the complete object. This outline, in its second stage, is drawn in a heavier, more visible line. The drawing can be developed graphically in still a third stage.

Drawing in crayon and charcoal produces a special character with pleasing graphic effects. As these drawings are not so precise as pencil or ink drawings, they are used only for design sketches, renderings, or details in large scale. These drawings are usually done freehand. They require a special paper and must be protected against smudging.

Drawing in ink. After a drawing is laid out in pencil, it can either be directly drawn over in ink, or it can be traced in ink on a sheet of translucent paper. Although the latter method saves one the trouble of erasing the original pencil lines, drawing in ink directly over the pencil lines is more precise. The pencil lines can often be left. A prerequisite for a good ink drawing is a clean drawing instrument in good condition. During the course of a drawing, ruling pens or ink-filler pens are periodically cleaned with a moist piece of buckskin, chamois, or sponge (textiles leave threads) so that the ink will flow uniformly and the line weight remain constant.

Drawings in different materials. For certain graphic effects, several techniques are combined (for example, pencil and ink, ink and colored pencils or watercolors). A good draftsman will usually try to finish a good pencil or ink drawing using only one technique and one type of material.

Erasing. Badly drawn or inaccurate lines must be erased. The density or hardness of the eraser to be used will de-

pend upon the type of paper and the pencil lead used. If an eraser smears (try it out first), rub off or cut away a piece of the surface. Smeared areas in the drawing are cleaned with erasers of different hardness. For drawings that are almost completed, the use of an erasing shield is recommended to isolate the area to be corrected. Ink lines are erased in three stages. As much as possible of the ink is initially removed with a sharp knife edge or a fiber-glass eraser. The remainder is then erased with an ink eraser. The area is then treated with a soft eraser and, finally, smoothed with a hard object. In the process, the paper surface should be damaged no more than is necessary. It must be possible to draw a clean ink line again over the erased area. [**Note:** If the paper is roughed up in the process of erasing ink it is often helpful to rub over the area with another piece of paper with the same finish before attempting to redraw the line.]

Drawing freehand or with instruments. The draftsman must also be able to draw freehand neatly and correctly. Some companies place particular worth on freehand drawing and may even have precise technical drawings redone freehand. Design sketches are always drawn freehand. The freehand drawing is the direct transposition from imagination to paper. It is more flexible, more expressive, and more graphic than a mechanical drawing. Architectural drawings, however, especially working drawings, are always completed with drawing instruments, though it is possible to lay out a drawing with instruments and then complete it freehand.

Types and methods of drawing. The most important types of architectural drawing and the most practical methods of executing them are as follows:

Design sketches without dimensions	Freehand in pencil, ink, pastels, or charcoal
Preliminary drawing with partial dimensions given	Freehand or mechanical in pencil or ink
Working drawings (including mechanical and electrical) with all dimensions given	Mechanical, usually in pencil
Details and shop drawings with all dimensions given	All drawing techniques
Presentation drawings (renderings)	All drawing techniques

Uses of Line Weights

Normally, a technical drawing includes three line weights. First, the object is laid out with a lightweight line; then it is drawn with a medium-weight line; finally, all necessary heavy lines (such as section lines) are drawn. The lines should be drawn exactly. Heavy lines are drawn by repeating strokes rather than by exerting too much pressure on the pencil. In ink drawings, the weight of the line should be determined before it is drawn.

Line Weight	Use
Thin lines $\frac{1}{200}''$–$\frac{1}{150}''$	Extension line, dimension line, center line, break line, alternate position, material indication
Medium lines $\frac{1}{80}''$–$\frac{1}{60}''$	Visible outline, hidden outline
Heavy lines $\frac{1}{40}''$–$\frac{1}{30}''$	Section lines, cutting planes

Scale. The proportionate size between an illustration and the object defined is the scale of the drawing.

Use	English system	Metric system	Use	English system	Metric system
City and regional planning maps	1″ = 1,000′ (1 : 12,000)	1 : 10,000	Preliminary designs, presentation drawings	¹⁄₁₆″ = 1′0″ (1 : 192)	1 : 200
	1″ = 500′ (1 : 6,000)	1 : 5,000		⅛″ = 1′0″ (1 : 96)	1 : 100
	1″ = 200′ (1 : 2,400)	1 : 2,500	Working drawings	¼″ — 1′0″ (1 . 48)	1 . 50
	¹⁄₆₄″ — 1′0″ (1 . 708)	1 . 1,000		⅛″ = 1′0″ (1 : 96)	1 : 100
Site plans, preliminary studies landscape planning	¹⁄₆₄″ = 1′0″ (1 : 768)	1 : 1,000			
	¹⁄₃₂″ = 1′0″ (1 : 384)	1 : 500	Details, shop drawings	¾″ = 1′0″ (1 : 16)	1 : 20
	¹⁄₁₆″ = 1′0″ (1 : 192)	1 : 200		1½″ = 1′0″ (1 : 8)	1 : 10
				3″ = 1′0″ (1 : 4)	1 : 5
				12″ = 1′0″ (1 : 1)	1 : 1

Entering Dimensions

Dimensions must be written legibly. All dimensions necessary for understanding the drawing must be given. The required dimensions for the different scales are different. For scales 1″ = 1,000′ to ¹⁄₁₆″ = 1′0″, it is sufficient to indicate the general principal dimensions. In drawings for **building permits,** it is necessary to supply the following dimensions: (1) overall dimensions, (2) wall thickness, (3) column dimensions, (4) window and door openings, (5) stair widths—run and rise, (6) square footage (principal areas and total). In addition, it is necessary to have some general notes concerning the type of construction, materials, equipment, and lot use. Floor heights are given from finished floor to finished floor. Rectangular openings are indicated by the width times the height (in feet and inches); round openings are indicated by the diameter in feet and inches, plus the symbol for diameter. In the **working drawings,** the dimensions must be indicated very carefully and checked. To further avoid mistakes during construction, the remark "Contractor to confirm all dimensions on job site prior to construction" is usually inserted on all working drawings. The following dimensions are always necessary: (1) dimensions of walls, columns, and chimneys, (2) window and door openings, (3) center to center dimensions of openings, (4) stairway dimensions, (5) exact dimensions of wall and floor rough openings, size and locations, (6) finished floor height in relation to finished floor height of main floor, (7) door and window heights from finished floor, (8) room dimensions, (9) fall of ramps and sloped floors. In addition, technical notes and indication of the materials necessary to complete the construction must be shown.

Detail drawings and shop drawings require all dimensions, material indications, and construction requirements.

Dimension lines are lines parallel to the direction of measurement. The dimension is written in the center of the line in the same direction. The line may be broken to insert the dimension, but in architectural drawings, the number is usually written above the line.

Extension lines run perpendicular to the dimension lines, connecting them with the object described. Both lines should be drawn so that they are easily seen and so that the dimensions can be easily read.

Dimension-line endings identify the full length of the measured object or space. This ending must be both drawn and placed correctly, using a circle, dot, angular stroke, or arrowhead.

[**Note:** Building codes and practices are varied in the United States; the information contained here is for general guidance only. It is suggested that the reader refer to other books on the preparation of drawings. The "detail drawings" mentioned above are part of the working drawings, while "shop drawings" are prepared by the fabricator.]

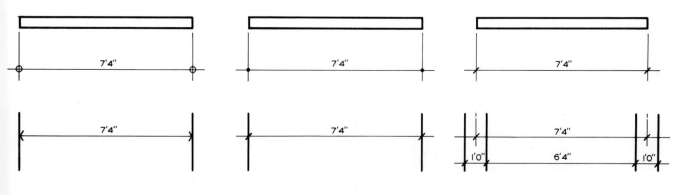

Lettering the Drawing

Each technical drawing must be lettered and dimensioned. Good lettering and dimensioning can improve the drawing and increase the overall graphic impression. By the same token, a lack of care and skill in lettering and dimensioning can ruin the best drawing. Notes on drawings should be brief and concise and provide information that cannot be learned from the drawing alone. In addition, the name of the job, the architect, the sheet number, the scale, and the date are lettered in. The lettering must be accurate and complete. The date alone can be very meaningful. The text can be lettered freehand or with lettering templates, or it can be drawn, constructed, stamped, or applied with ready-made letters. The method depends upon the character and purpose of the drawing. In all cases, the lettering must be legible and placed to be easily seen.

Lettering size. The size of the lettering must correspond to the sheet size. Lettering that serves to orient one within the sheet, such as labels, room designations, etc., should be larger than the notations of materials or dimensions. Lettering less than 3/32″ cannot be read easily. For important sheets, letters, lettering size, and distance between lines must be tested. It is also possible that a special style of lettering will have to be designed.

[**Note:** In the United States the job and architect identification on a drawing is often printed or rubber-stamped on each drawing. It is wise to remember that the upper half of a line of lettering alone tells more than the lower half. Short, wide letters also are more legible than tall thin ones.]

Lettering. Only a few hints are given here. Much practice and some knowledge of theory is necessary to letter well. There are excellent books on this subject. To create a new alphabet requires a great deal of both concentration and time because all letters must give the same impression and produce a unified composition when used in any combination. Standard lettering is usually used for technical drawings. Appropriate examples of both prepared letters and templates are available everywhere. For working drawings, there is no prescribed standard. The important thing is that plans can be lettered quickly and legibly. A good draftsman will strive to refine his lettering.

Constructed lettering falls under the rules of drawing technique insofar as its construction and execution is concerned. In the case of lettering for shops or public buildings, the lettering should be handled as any other regular working drawing.

Lettering Types

The Roman capital letters, in the refined Antiqua, are the origin of all Latin and Gothic alphabets. The proportion of the letters and their spacing make the composition. They are drawn here in their simple block letter form.
Using a square divided vertically and horizontally into six equal areas both ways, the letters of the alphabet have the following proportions: B E F L J K R P S, 3 : 6; A H N T U V X Y Z, 5 : 6; C D G O Q, 6 : 6; M W, 7 : 6. The outside angles of M and W are smaller than the inside angles.

The spacing of letters cannot be so accurately determined. In any event, areawise, the space between any two letters should be almost equal. The linear distance between two letters is not constant. Whereas the curves of OO almost touch, the vertical stems of NN are definitely separated.

For this reason, the area between any two successive vertical stems is used as a basis for spacing. If this space is increased or decreased, then the word appears extended or compressed, accordingly.

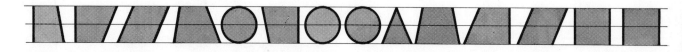

Character of lettering. Alphabets consist of letters with the same characterisitcs. The letters can be narrower or wider, the stems can be heavier or lighter; they can be vertical or inclined. Also, the O's must relate to the character of the lettering selected.

Line spacing considerably determines the total impression of a composition. Letter heights and line spacing are initially ruled with thin guide lines. Line spacing should be at least letter height in order for large letters to be legible. Here are several variations of the alphabet used throughout this book.

regular

ABCDEFGH
abcdefghijkl

semibold

ABCDEFGH
abcdefghijkl

bold

ABCDEFG
abcdefghij

condensed

ABCDEFGHIJKL
abcdefghijklmn

oblique

ABCDEFGH
abcdefghijkl

semibold extended

ABCDEFG
abcdefghi

regular

1234567890

bold

123456789

oblique

1234567890

Certain standard information is consolidated in a title block placed in the lower righthand corner of the sheet. [**Note:** The number and date of the most recent revision is always entered at the top of the title block. Earlier drawings should be discarded to avoid confusion.]

Name and address of office			
Title of drawing (Floor Plan, etc.) and scale			
Drawn by	Date	Checked by	Date
Approved	Date	Revision	Date
Plan No.		Sheet ____ of ____	

Name and address of job						Plan No.	
Title of drawing (Floor Plan, etc.)						Scale	
Drawn by	Date	Checked by	Date	Approved	Date	Revision	Date
Name and address of office						Sheet ____ of ____	

A. Simple Projection

A Simple Projection

Methods and Use

All technical drawings have a common basis—a system—upon which they are developed: the projection. In this case, the projection is the relationship between a point in space and its representation on a selected plane (plane of projection, drawing board, drawing paper, etc.). The science which deals with the laws of projection and the rules of drawing technology is *descriptive geometry,* established by Gaspard Monge (1746–1818).

That part of descriptive geometry which is related to build-ing construction technology is important in architectural drawing. The projection of simple bodies on one or more planes is treated in this section. Beginning with the general principles of descriptive geometry, the methods and laws by which a technical drawing is developed are covered. The examples show the relationship between the actual or assumed object and its technical illustration.

Construction lines and auxiliary planes are definite drawing and thinking aids, which, when wisely used, simplify drawing problems and in many cases set up a good control for the correctness and exactness of the drawing.

A1 Types of Projections

To represent a point or a line in space, the point or line is projected with straight lines (called projection rays or simply projectors) onto one or two planes. (This is comparable to film projection and light rays.) The points where the projectors pierce the picture plane outline the projected object.

a Projection on a vertical (frontal) plane.
If a point in space is projected on a plane which, in each direction lies perpendicular to the direction of the projection, the projection is then called **perpendicular projection.** Projection under any other given angle is called **oblique projection** (illustrated with broken lines).

b Projection on a horizontal plane (plan) can also be executed as a perpendicular or oblique projection.
The planes of projection can be inclined at any angle. The deciding factor for the difference between the perpendicular and the oblique projection is the angle of projection, not the position of the plane of projection.

Parallel Projection

c If two points of a straight line are projected onto a plane by perpendicular projectors, the projectors of both points are parallel lines, and the projection is called **vertical or horizontal parallel projection.** If the two points are projected onto the plane under any other angle, the projectors remain parallel, and the projection is an **oblique parallel projection.**

Central Projection

d The projection can also take place with projectors which stem from one point. This point can be assumed as desired. Contrary to parallel projection, the projection of the lines or figures varies in size, and this variance is directly relative to the change in the distance of the plane of projection from the projected object. This method of projection is called **central projection.**
The central projection is the basis of all perspectives.

The Projection of a Straight Line on Two Planes

e Here is a straight line which lies in space parallel to the frontal plane and inclined to the horizontal plane. It is projected by parallel projection onto a horizontal and a vertical plane. Revolve one of the planes until it lies in the same plane as the other. Both projections thus appear in the same plane, one directly above the other.

f Projection of the straight line in **e,** above, on the vertical (frontal or profile) plane and on the horizontal (top view or plan) plane. In elevation the projection of a point always lies directly vertical above its projection in plan, and vice versa. Here the straight line appears in its true size only in elevation. In plan it appears shortened.

g A straight line is as in **f,** above, but suspended in space and inclined to both frontal and horizontal planes. The line is projected onto the vertical and horizontal planes by parallel projection.

h Projection of the straight line in **g,** above. It appears shortened in both planes. See A6 **c–f** for the method of determining its true size.

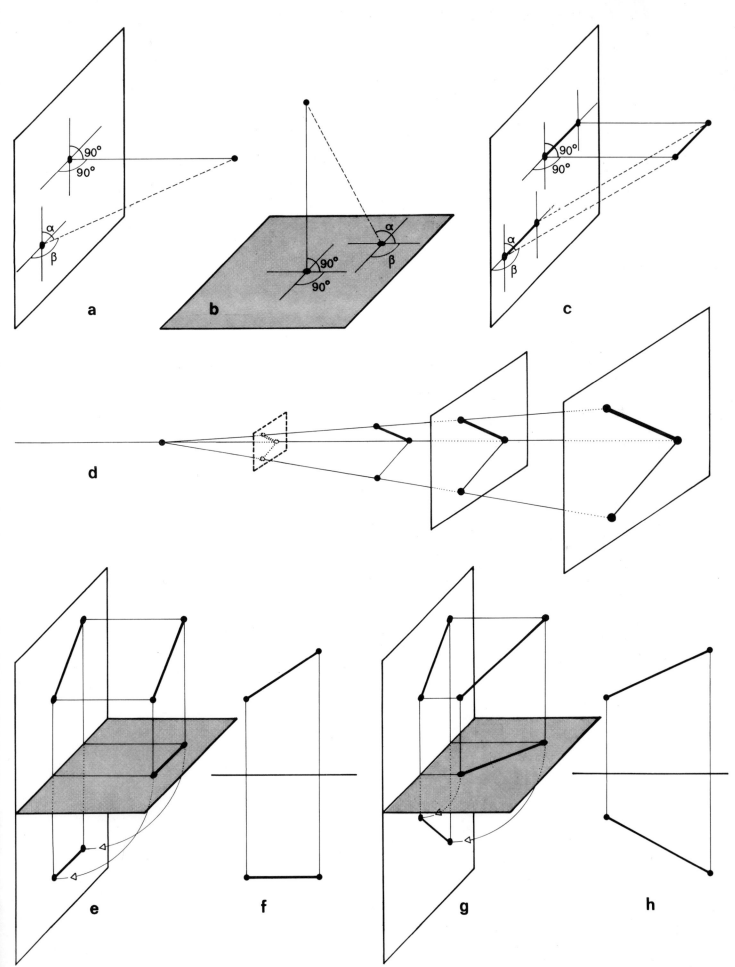

A2   Orthographic Projection

Orthographic projection has been developed into a system which ordinarily consists of three principal planes: plan or **horizontal plane,** front elevation or **frontal plane,** and side elevation or **profile plane.**

These planes can also be constructed as cutting planes, intersecting the object where desired and thus revealing a section view. These sections are named, according to the principal direction of the object intersected, longitudinal section or cross section, and, according to the cutting plane, horizontal or vertical section. Cutting planes are also used as auxiliary planes for various constructions (see A8 **c–e** and A10 **e–f**).

The projection of any given point in front elevation lies perpendicular above its projection in plan, and at the same height as its projection in side elevation or section.

First Angle Projection (European standard)

a According to the European standard, the principal planes of projection lie below, behind, and beside the object. The projection is accomplished by sight rays or projectors from the viewer passing through all points of the object onto the corresponding plane.

b When the front elevation and the plan are rotated into a common plane, the front elevation lies above the plan, the side elevation, correspondingly right or left, at the same height as the front elevation.

Third Angle Projection (U.S. standard)

c According to the American standard, the principal planes of projection lie above, in front of, and beside the object. The projection is made by projectors from all points on the object passing through the corresponding plane to the viewer.

d When the frontal plane is rotated into the horizontal plane (or vice versa), the plan lies above the front elevation, and the side elevation lies to the left or right of it at the same height as the front elevation.

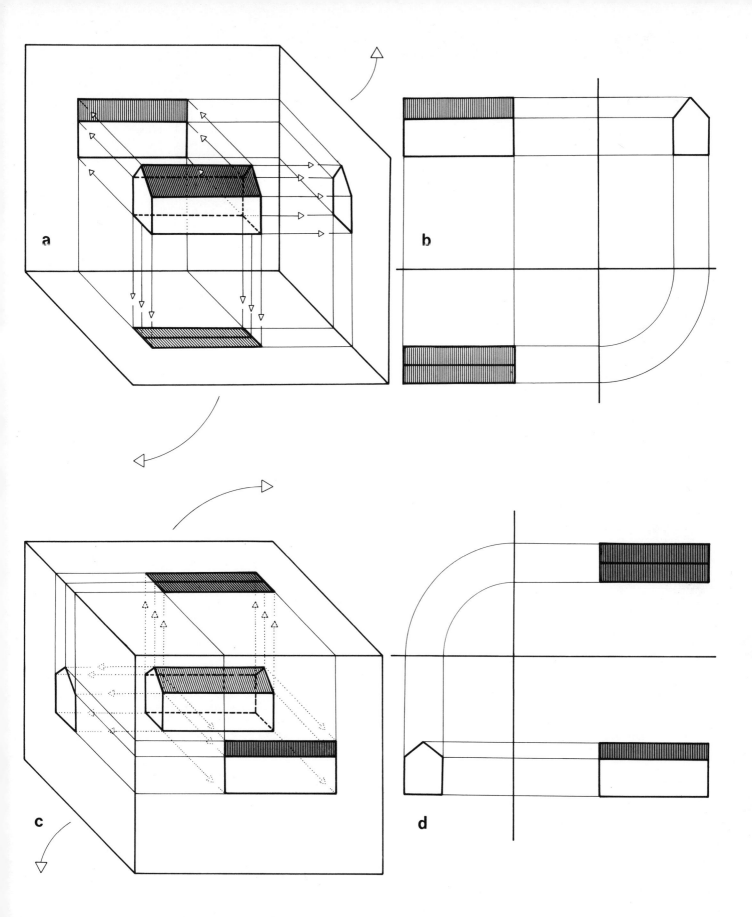

A3 Orthographic Projection and the Architectural Drawing

The drawing standards outlined in A2 are not always practical in drawing a set of building plans. In architectural drawing, however, readability is more important than standards.

a The outline of a building is shown in a_1, a_2, and a_3. The front elevation lies below the plan. Reference A2 **b,** according to the European standard relative position of views in third-angle projection, a_3 should have the position of the right side elevation. However, the relationship of the elevations to each other and to the plan is much more readily recognized when the left side elevation is shown. Just as in this example, one should always try to accomplish clear, readable architectural drawings.

Elevation and Plan

b Objects with the same front elevation can appear quite different in plan. In order to determine the form of an object, both the plan and the elevation are necessary in almost all cases. With reference to the object in b_3, even the side elevation is necessary for a clear illustration.

c The cube appears as a square in all three projections (plan and front and side elevations).

Elevation of a Rotated Plan

d When the cube is rotated in plan, two surfaces appear in the front elevation. The illustration looks better but the measurements are more difficult to determine, since both length and width appear foreshortened. The front elevation of an object with only its corner in the picture plane is the simplest way of indicating its three dimensions.

Isometric Drawing

e The front elevation of the cube is combined with two other views—both with unshortened dimensions—in oblique parallel projection. The angle of projection (45°) and the width : depth : height proportions in the three principal directions are indicated in the symbol below the drawing.

The result is a pictorial (three-dimensional) view of the cube, which appears oversized in depth. In general, this method of drawing is known as *isometric projection;* the specific 45° angle of projection is also known as *cavalier projection.* The isometric projection is always developed from the front elevation of the object illustrated.

In the front elevation, the dimensions are unchanged. Also unchanged are the dimensions along the indicated angle of projection (45°). However, the dimensions change on all diagonals which do not lie in the front elevation plane. The illustration of the object looks better, but it loses some of the exactness of its dimensions.

f Isometric projection of a cube with a 30° angle of projection, unforeshortened.

Isometric Projection with Foreshortened Depth Dimension

From illustrations **e** and **f,** it is evident that the cube appears elongated in depth when this dimension is drawn full length. In order to make the proportions look more realistic, the depth dimension is often foreshortened in oblique and axonometric drawings.

g Isometric projection of a cube with a 30° angle of projection, foreshortened. The depth dimension is shown here at one-half scale. The cube appears more correct in size, but creates some inconsistency in reading true sizes from the drawing. The amount of foreshortening of the depth dimension may be selected as desired. For the proper illustration, try to find the scale which appears most pleasing optically.

False Perspective

h The false perspective might be referred to as a simplified trimetric (three unequal axes) drawing. The front elevation is forced out of its right angle, and the top and side views are drawn with a 30° angle of projection with the depth dimension at one-half scale. Thus it appears more pictorial but loses still more in exact dimensions, because the diagonals of the front elevation are now distorted. In front elevation, the angle of distortion should not vary more than 6° from the right angle.

The Isometric Plan

i The isometric layout plan is a special axonometric drawing in which the plan and sections in planes parallel thereto retain their true shapes and dimensions (as does the front elevation of the oblique projection), but which is rotated so that only one corner appears in the picture plane. By this method, a cube is drawn. In this case, the two mutually perpendicular edges make angles of 60° and 30°, respectively, with the picture plane.

Height dimensions are laid out vertically from each corner. The completed drawing shows the top view as a repetition of the plan view and shows the side elevation (corresponding to the symbol below it) with unchanged height dimensions. However, diagonal dimensions of the sides are distorted, like all isometric drawings whose sides are not parallel to the picture plane. This type of drawing is sometimes erroneously referred to as a bird's-eye perspective; that is, a three-point perspective view of an object from above. The height in the illustration appears exaggerated, just as does the depth in **e** and **f** above.

k The same cube is illustrated with the height dimensions foreshortened to one-half scale. The drawing appears more correct in its overall impression, although it is even less accurate in its dimensions. The ratio of reduced height to actual height may be selected as desired.

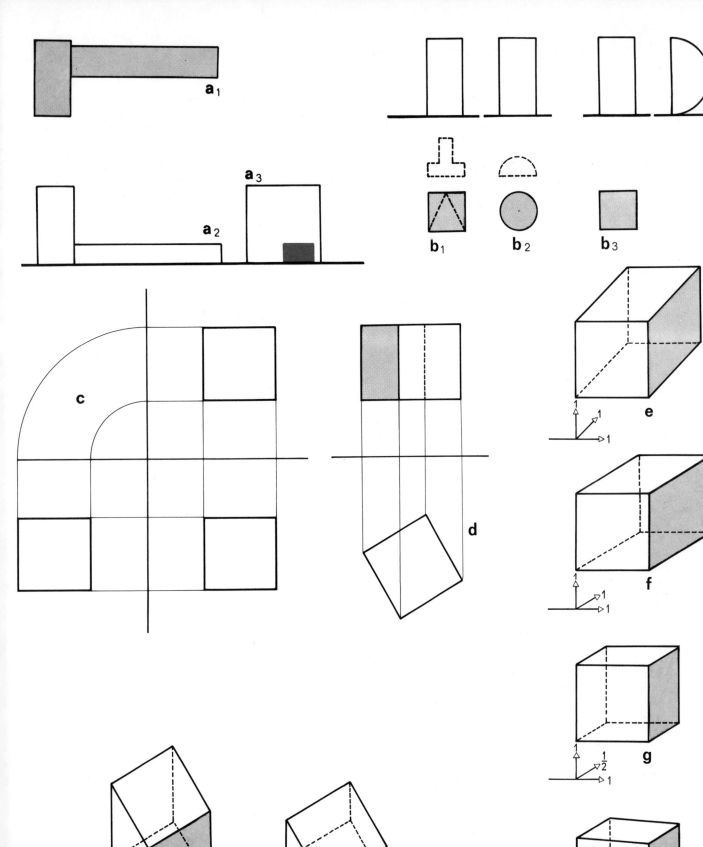

a_1

a_2

a_3

b_1

b_2

b_3

c

d

e

f

g

h

i

k

A4 Isometric Drawing of Circular Forms

Orthographic and Isometric Views of a Circle

a Above: an unforeshortened isometric view, with oblique axis at an angle of 45° to the horizontal. Below: an unforeshortened isometric view, with oblique axis at an angle of 30° to the horizontal. In each case the isometric view of the circle is an ellipse. The principal axes of the circles are, in their isometric views, conjugate diameters of their corresponding ellipses. Compare A14 **c, g.**

b A cylinder in elevation and plan.

Isometric View of a Cylinder

c Corresponding to the direction of the principal axes of the circumscribed rectangular solid, the individual construction points are laid out. The top and plan views (circles) become ellipses, and their vertical tangents establish the borderlines.

Isometric Plan of a Cylinder

d The midpoint of the top view of the cylinder is located veritcally above the midpoint of the plan of the cylinder. The height is not foreshortened and thus appears exaggerated. This construction compares with A3 **i.**

e Isometric plan (as in **d,** above) is illustrated one-half actual height. However, the proportion of reduction may be selected as desired.

f Isometric plan, one-half actual height (as in **e,** above), but with principal axis inclined (thus, an oblique view). This makes the drawing appear more three-dimensional. The example is illustrated as a hollow cylinder (e.g., as in the top view of a glass).

Isometric Drawing of a Sphere

g The sphere is inscribed within a cube (g_1). An oblique view of the sphere's sections is drawn for each vertical (broken line) and horizontal (dot-dash line) section plane (plan, g_2; elevation, g_3). These section views appear as vertical (broken line) and horizontal (dot-dash line) ellipses. A continuous curve constructed around both vertical and horizontal ellipses establishes an isometric view of the sphere, also an ellipse.

Isometric Plan of a Sphere

h The unforeshortened height corresponds to the vertical diameter of the sphere. The radius of the sphere is marked off vertically above and below the midpoint of the base circle, the plan view. At selected heights, cutting planes are passed through the sphere (elevation, h_3; plan, h_2). Necessary measurements for each section are transferred to the perspective, and the cross sections (circles) are drawn at their respective heights. A continuous curve tangent to the outermost circles results in the isometric plan of the sphere, an ellipse. By appropriate foreshortening of the height, the resultant isometric plan becomes a circle.

Cross Vaults Developed from Circular Forms

i A square plan and corresponding elevation of a cross vault. (See C14, C15.)

k An isometric plan of a cross vault with unforeshortened heights shows a view from above. The construction compares with A3 **i.** The circular arches appear as ellipses, as do the diagonals. (See C14.)

l A reversed isometric plan of the cross vault in **k,** above, as viewed from below. Illustrated is a view through the left front arch from the bottom of the cross vault (interior view).

All systems of pictorial drawing can be used to construct views from above as well as from below.

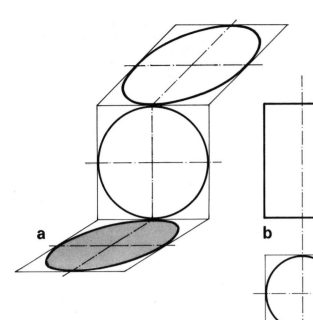

a

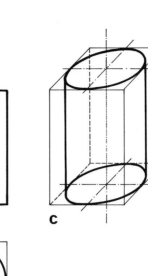

b

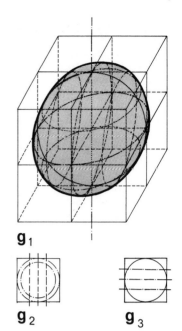

c

g₁

g₂   g₃

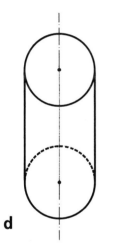

d

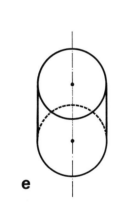

e

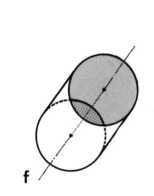

f

h₂

h₃   h₁

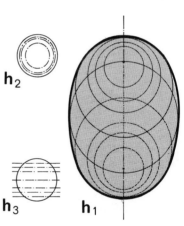

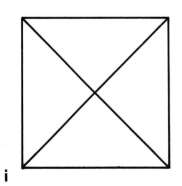

i

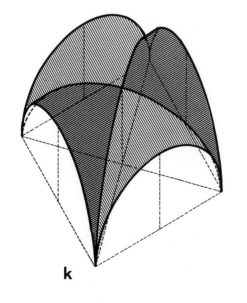

k

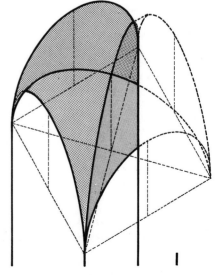

l

A5 Uniplanar Method (Map and Topographic Drawing)

a The uniplanar (one plane) method is the scale drawing of objects in one plane. The location of the object is drawn in the plane and its height given in numbers (compare A1 **b**). The uniplanar method is used primarily in maps, surveys, and plans for underground construction.

The Slope Cone

b The origin of the slope cone. Each solid material has a certain slump, which is dependent upon different factors. If the material is the same, the slump angle is less in stacking or piling than in digging out, and these angles vary depending upon grain size and whether the material is dry or wet.

c A slope cone with the angle of slope α, in plan, elevation, and isometric view. The slope plane is drawn to the left of the slope cone in isometric.

Contour Lines

d Plan and pictorial view of mountainous terrain with contour lines. For the representation of terrain all points at the same height are connected by a contour line. The contour lines are thus sections through the terrain at a certain height, relative to normal sea level, 0. Contour lines are most frequently used in map drafting, plot plans, and underground construction work.

A Horizontal Street Intersecting a Hill

e Terrain with given contour lines is cut through by a street which runs at Elevation 355. The street cuts through the terrain above Elevation 355 and runs over a filled embankment where the terrain is lower than Elevation 355. The embankment slope for the excavation (e_2) is α, for the fill (e_3) β. The horizontal distances a and b, corresponding to the elevations concerned, are drawn in. Lines representing the horizontal distances run parallel to the street. Connect the points of intersection of these lines with the natural contour lines. The resulting line is the intersection of the terrain and the embankment.

An Evenly Ascending Street at Level Grade

f The incline for the corresponding contour lines is constructed by means of a slope cone. The radius of the slope cone increases by c from contour line to contour line. Connect the outermost intersections of the contour lines with the base semicircle of the slope cone. The resulting line is the intersection of the terrain and the embankment, and by connecting similar intersections at each successive interval, the contour lines of the embankment are established.

Illustration of Slopes

g Slopes are indicated in different ways. In cartography the method of illustration is indicated on the map itself, usually by contour lines, hatching, or toning.

A frequently used method of illustration is shown by g_1, with g_3, g_5, and g_6 as variants. Contour lines are shown by g_2, and a combination of contour lines and toning is shown by g_4. The toning can be purely graphic or in color. Slopes are illustrated differently on a small-scale plot plan than on a large-scale plan.

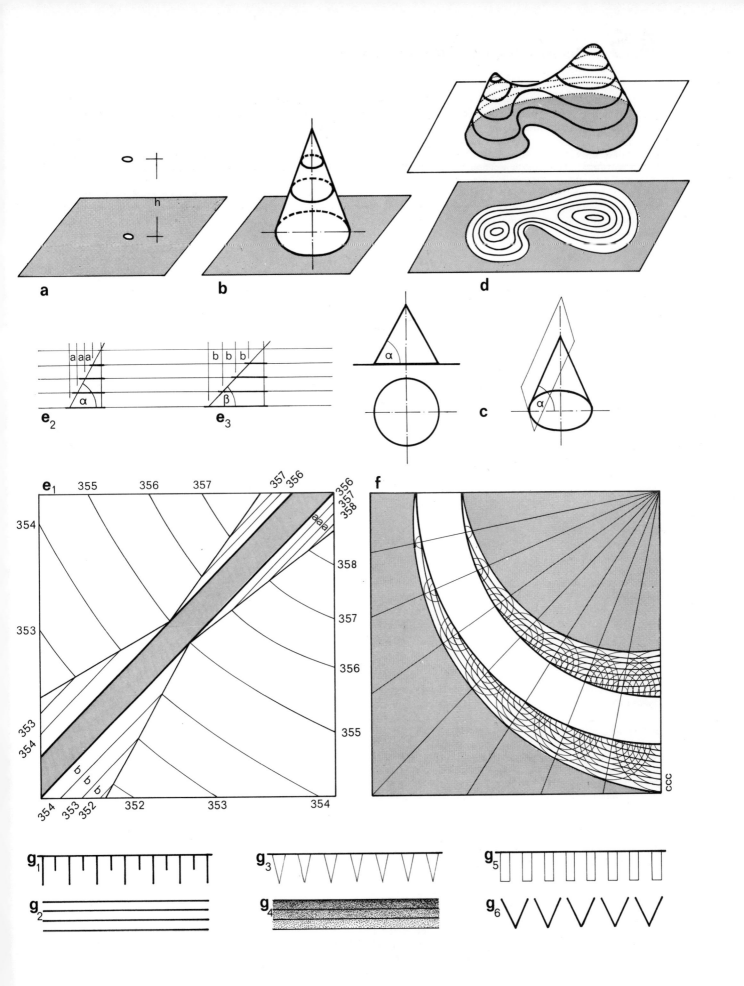

a

b

d

e₂

e₃

c

e₁

355   356   357   357 356   356
                                 357
                                 358

354

                                 358

353   357

                                 356

353
354   355

σ
ϱ
ϱ

354 353 352   352   353   354

f

CCC

g₁

g₂

g₃

g₄

g₅

g₆

27

A6 Determining True Sizes and Shapes

The true length of a line or size of an area is the basis for its technical illustration. This cannot always be determined directly from the plan and elevation.

a Pictorial drawing of a line in space which lies parallel to the horizontal plane and is inclined to the frontal plane. (See also A1 **e, f.**)

b Plan and elevation of the same line. It appears in its true length only in plan. In the elevation it appears foreshortened because of its oblique position.

Determining True Size and Shape by Rotation of a Plane

c Pictorial drawing of an inclined straight line suspended in space. This line is inclined to the horizontal plane and to the picture plane. (See A1 **g, h.**)

d This line appears foreshortened by the inclination in plan and elevation. In order to determine its true size, in its vertical plane it is rotated into the horizontal plane. A line whose length is equal to h, the difference in height between the lowest and the highest points along the line in elevation, is laid out in plan at an angle of 90°. The side connecting the free ends of the two established sides reveals the true size or length (dot-dash line).

Determining True Size and Shape by Rotation of a Line

e Isometric drawing of an inclined straight line suspended in space (as in **c**) inclined in both horizontal and frontal planes.

f In this case, the straight line is rotated in plan on the end nearest to the picture plane until it is parallel to the picture plane. The uppermost point is thereby moved horizontally forward, in elevation. The rotated line then appears in its projection in elevation in its true length (dot-dash line).

Determining the True Size of a Triangle by Rotation of Each Individual Side

g A triangle in plan and elevation (heavy lines). The triangle lies inclined to both planes in elevation and plan, thus all side dimensions appear foreshortened. To determine their true lengths, draw each individual side in plan as illustrated in **d,** above. When the true size of all three sides of the triangle are determined, use them to draw the triangle (dot-dash line).

Determining the True Size of a Triangle by Rotation of the Entire Triangle in the Horizontal Plane

h A triangle in plan and elevation, as in **g**, above. The true size is determined by rotation of the entire triangle in the horizontal plane, in accordance with the following:
1 The sides of the triangle in elevation are extended to the horizontal plane. The extended lines produce two points of intersection with the horizontal plane, A and B. The line AB in plan provides the axis of rotation about which the triangle is to be rotated.

2 Perpendicular to this axis, an auxiliary plane is constructed so that it touches the apex of the triangle (broken line).
3 This auxiliary plane, in which lies the vertical height of the triangle's apex h above the horizontal plane and the distance from the triangle's apex to the axis of rotation CS, is now also rotated in the horizontal plane.
4 The distance of the triangle's apex from the axis of rotation CS is transferred in true size from the axis downward.
5 The points of intersection of the extended sides are connected with the resulting triangle's apex, S, according to (4), above.
6 The true distance between the other two angles is determined according to (3), above, and also transferred below, as the apex of the triangle according to (5), above. In this manner, the three corner points of the triangle are rotated in the horizontal plane at their true distances, and the true size of the triangle is established (dot-dash line).

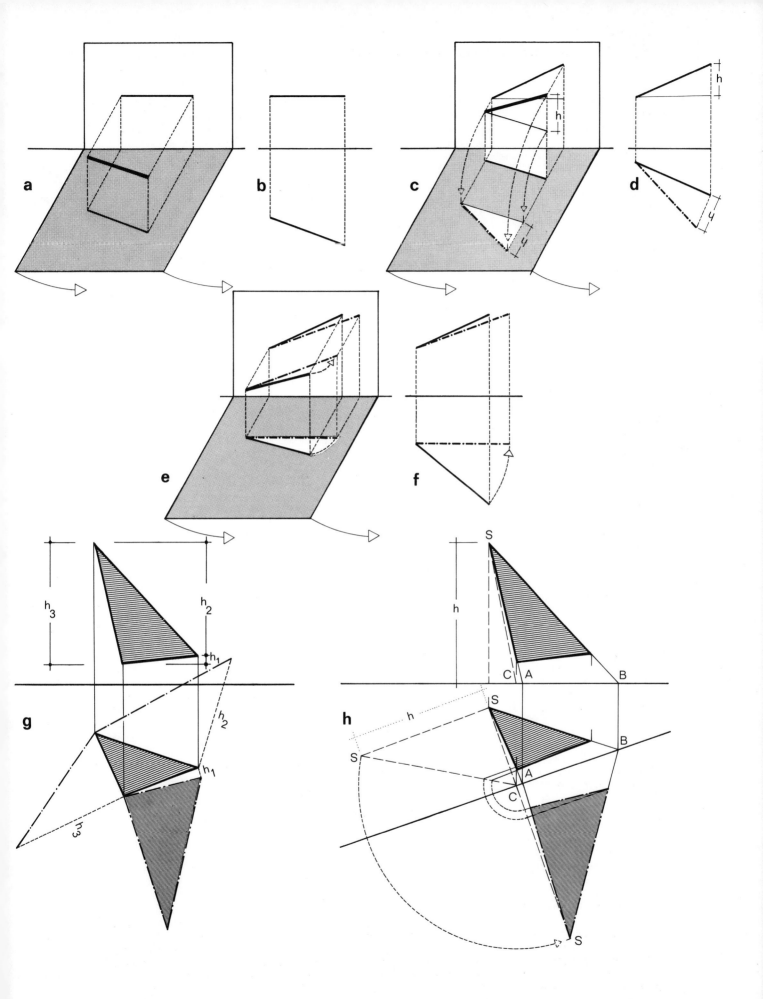

In the development of roof types, the geometrical relationship and construction are best explained graphically. Determining the true size of roof areas, slopes, etc. is necessary even for the simplest paper model. The basic geometrical form of a roof is referred to as its type.

Gable Roof

a The simplest roof type is the gable roof with two planes. The lower horizontal edge, parallel to the length of the roof, is known as the eave. The inclined edge, parallel to the width of the roof, is known as the pitch. The intersection, or peak, of the two roof planes is the ridge.

Hip Roof

b The simplest roof type with a continuous eave on all four sides is the hip roof. The inclined intersection between two roof planes is called the hip for exterior angles and the valley for interior angles.

Determining the True Length of the Hip by Rotation of a Plane

c A hip roof in plan and elevation. The true length of the hip is determined by rotation—that is, in plan, the height h of the hip is laid out from the upper end of the hip at an angle of 90°. In other words, the line h, with top end F, is revolved about its base into the horizontal plane, perpendicular to the hip. The line (dot-dash) connecting point F with the base of the hip is the true length of the hip.

d This is the same hip roof as in **c,** above. The true length of the hip is determined by rotating the hip in plan until it lies parallel to the picture plane. The new endpoint of the hip is projected to the elevation view. The new line (heavy dot-dash line) connecting the base with the ridge is the true length of the hip.

Determining the True Size of Hip Areas by Rotation into the Horizontal Plane

e Using the eave line as an axis, each respective area is rotated into the horizontal plane. The left hip area—which is at a right angle to the picture plane—is rotated directly into the horizontal plane. For the right hip area—which is oblique to the picture plane—pass a vertical cutting plane through the hip area extending from the ridge to the eave (F to T) and perpendicular to the eave line. This vertical section, when rotated about its base into the horizontal plane, reveals the true length of line FT, the altitude of the desired triangular area. With both the length of the eave (the base) and the altitude FT known, the true size of the hip area can now be determined.

Roofs of Irregular Floor Plans

f In an irregular plan, a roof with constant slope is lower on the narrow end of the gable roof and higher on the wide end. This produces an inclined ridge and a different length for each rafter. The ridge line is extended as a bisector between the two roof surfaces. The true slope α of the roof area runs perpendicular to this bisector. If both roof surfaces have the same slope and, in plan, the gable ends are not perpendicular to the ridge, then the ridge does not lie in the middle of the gable ends. The ends of the ridge must then be constructed from the plan with their heights indicated by the cross-section triangles (thin lines).

Should the ridge line run horizontally, then the roof slope changes constantly; over the narrowest end stands the steepest slope, and over the widest end, the lowest slope (dotted line). For the roof area, this produces a twisted or warped plane and different rafter lengths. It is, in addition, a more difficult construction to roof a warped area.

Simplest Roof Type for an Irregular Floor Plan

g With an irregular hip roof (all hips meeting at one point) over the same plan as in **f,** four straight roof surfaces are created, illustrated by triangles. Although the rafters are also of different lengths in this case, the areas allow themselves, as triangles, to be neatly constructed and roofed. Water drainage from an irregular area is a geometrical problem with courts, terraces, and other building areas as well as roofs. For exterior drainage, water can be drained toward the edges; for interior drainage, it can be drained to a point near the center to which all areas slope (dot-dash line).

Roof Layout with Eave Line of Constant Height

h Illustrated is a building with a hip roof, with a smaller wing added to it. The eave line is at the same height on both wings of the building. All roof areas are of the same slope, so the hips and valleys appear in plan as bisectors of the mutually perpendicular eave lines. The top view of the roof planes is called the roof layout. This layout is drawn best from the widest span to the narrowest. The intersection of two roof surfaces which meet at an interior angle of the roof is a valley, which corresponds to the valley rafter. (See A9 **e.**)

The Roof Layout with Eave Lines of Varying Height

i A building with a hip roof, and a smaller wing added which has a lower eave line. The roof layout of the larger building is a simple hip roof, as is the layout of the smaller addition. The long sides of the small roof in part intersect the main house wall and in part the larger roof surface. The intersection is found in the elevation. If the areas of the small and the large roofs have the same slope, all hips and valleys are drawn at an angle of 45°.

[**Note:** This section and the two following are scarcely applicable to architecture as practiced in the United States today. However, mastery of the fundamentals of orthographic projection and perspective drawing as expounded elsewhere in the book will make it possible for the draftsman to draw any modern roof form.]

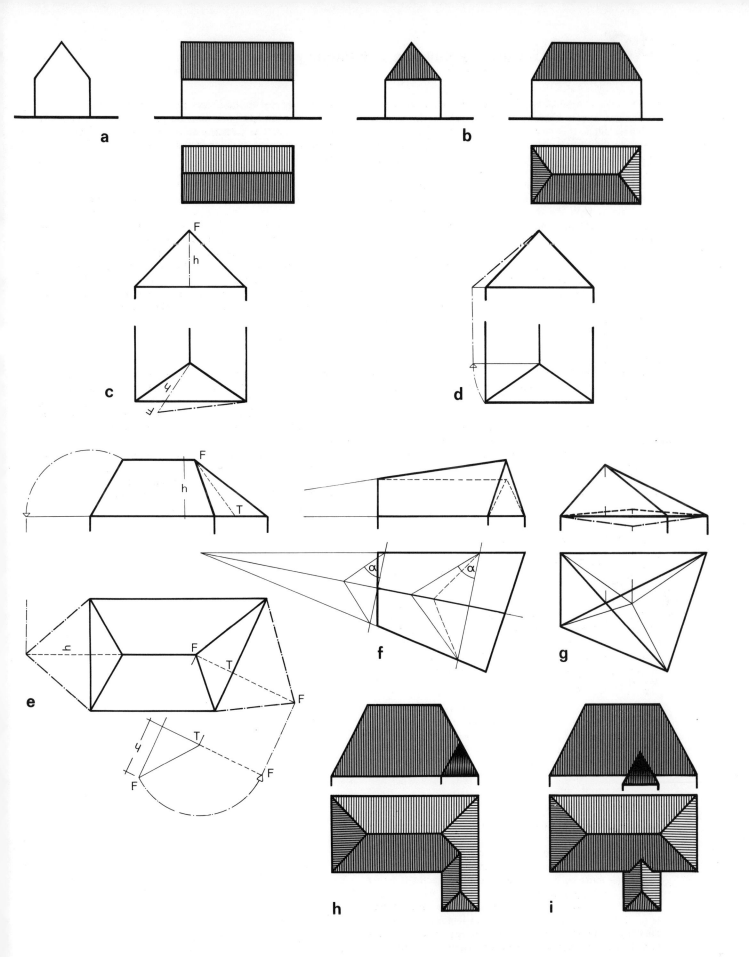

a The plan of a building with three adjacent sides having two obtuse angles between them. All roof surfaces have the same pitch. This means that the hip (or valley) can be drawn as the bisector of the two adjacent eave lines from all eave corners. The roof layout can now be drawn except for the length of the valley and the hip between the two ridges. In order to determine the valley and the hip, the eave lines are extended until they intersect. The bisector of the angle is both the direction of the hip and the hip's intersection with the valley. The connection of this hip-valley intersection to the ridge of the small addition results in the corresponding hip. This construction is only possible, however, when all roof slopes are the same.

In other cases, construct a section at selected point A, perpendicular to the eave of the irregular side. The desired hip line goes through the apex C of the established section triangle. The triangle side from A, rotated in plan, is established by the given roof slope. Angle ABF is determined when one erects a perpendicular to the ridge line from the intersection of the auxiliary cutting plane and the extended ridge line. Point C, the intersection of both sides, is then projected to the cutting plane. A line from the ridge through C is the desired hip line.

b This is the same plan as in **a**, above, but with a flat roof and interior drainage. One has to consider here that the lines corresponding to ridge lines must have the necessary fall in order to shed water. Just as with a roof, drainage must be provided for courts or other outside areas, streets, and walks.

The True Angle Between Two Roof Areas

The true angle formed by two adjacent planes is measured perpendicular to their common intersection. On a roof, this is the angle perpendicular to the hip line.

c Isometric illustration of the cutting angle α between both roof surfaces. The cutting plane, in which the desired angle lies, is perpendicular to the hip rafter, and, from the roof, defines the triangle ABC, which is rotated into the horizontal plane where the true size of the angle is revealed.

d The line AB of the section triangle is drawn perpendicular to the hip in plan. Then the height h and the true length and slope of the hip are determined by rotation. The point C is found by constructing a line perpendicular to the rotated hip from point D in plan. The line CD is the height of the triangle ABC'. The angle AC'B is the true angle between both roof surfaces.

Intersection of an Inclined Plane and a Vertical Line

e An upright stands on a roof plane. Its position is fixed in plan. In the elevation above it, its intersection with the roof plane must be drawn. This intersection point is found through auxiliary constructions. In plan, a cutting plane from eave to ridge is passed through this straight line (e.g., lines 1-1, 2-2, 3-3); that is, one imagines a vertical auxiliary plane which cuts through the roof area. In elevation, this cutting plane (between eave and ridge) cuts the vertical line at its point of intersection with the roof surface.

If a body, such as a dormer or chimney (broken line), inter-

sects the roof surface, the points of intersection of the individual straight lines and the roof surface are similarly constructed. The cutting planes are laid to best advantage when they pass through the intersecting surfaces of the body (lines 4-4 and 5-5).

Intersection of an Inclined Plane with an Inclined Line

f Isometric of an inclined plane (gray tone), which is pierced by an inclined line (thick line). In order to determine the point of intersection, construct an auxiliary plane which cuts through the straight line (thick line) perpendicular to the horizontal plane. This cuts the inclined plane in a straight line. The intersection of this straight line with the inclined line (thick line) is the desired point of intersection.

Roof Layout

Roof layout is referred to as the geometrical relationship of the surfaces of a roof. The gable roof is one of the simplest types. With the selection of a hip roof, one has the choice of making all roof surfaces of the same slope or of making the end and side surfaces of different slopes. In plan the hip line is the bisector of the angle made by two intersecting eave lines only if all roof surfaces have the same pitch (slope). The more irregular a building is, the more complicated the roof layout will be.

If the roof pitch is varied, construct the hip lines individually in plan, elevation, and side view or section.

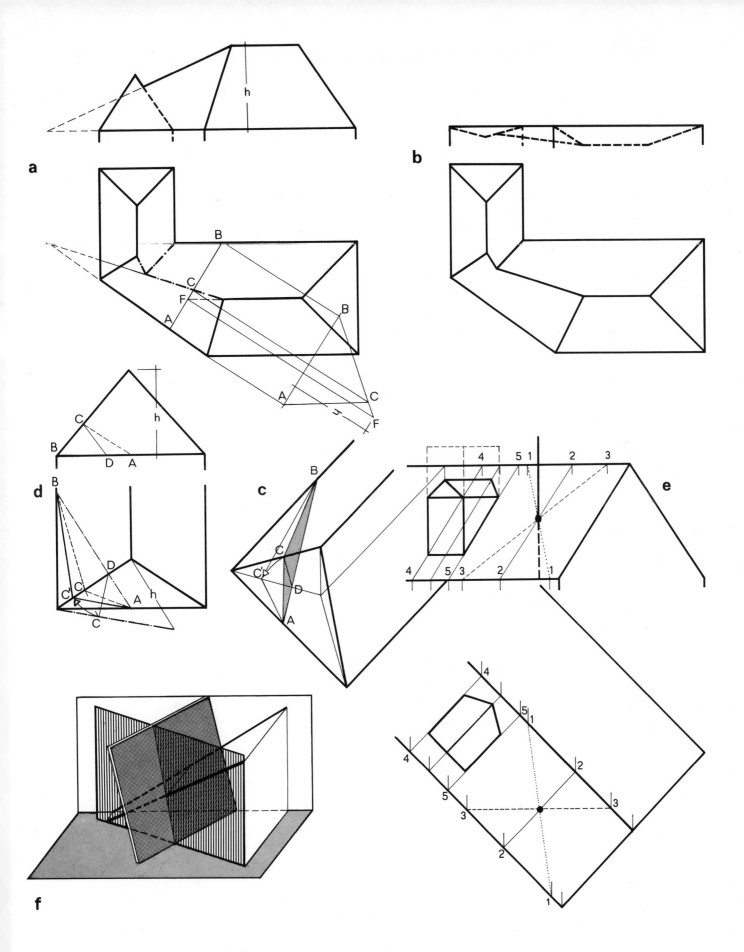

A9 True Length of Hip and Valley Rafters

Determining the True Length of the Hip Rafter

a Isometric view of a corner of a hip roof with hip rafter. The true length of the hip rafter and its exact detailing are important for the architect to know. Its length and the height of its vertical cross section are dependent upon the roof pitch.

b A rafter in elevation and in plan. The true length is determined by rotation in plan. The rafter is rotated parallel to the picture plane (see A7 **d**). The height of the hip rafter is dependent upon the height of the common rafters. To construct this height, a rafter of the steepest roof area (from the end hip surface, in this case) is rotated in plan so that its true angle appears in the elevation. The depth (d) of the rafter is the length of its perpendicular cross-sectional area. The height (h), which is to be nailed to the hip rafter, can be determined from the depth (d).

The details at the corner of the house and at the ridge must be particularly noted. The corner rafter ends will have to be cut in different lengths (a and b), because of the different roof slopes. This must be thoroughly detailed.

c Isometric view of the hip rafter, lower section and rafter end illustrated.

Determining the True Length of the Valley Rafter

d Isometric view of a roof valley. The roof valley construction is illustrated by a valley rafter. As in **b,** the length and the construction height are dependent upon the roof pitch.

e Valley rafters in elevation and plan. Determining the true size by rotation as in **b,** above. The ridge and eave must be correspondingly detailed.

f Isometric view of the valley rafter, corresponding to **c,** above. The examples drawn here are basic carpentry construction. However, wood-roof construction can also be carried out as an engineered, laminated, or nailed construction. Other roof construction can be of steel and reinforced concrete. The true sizes, heights, and angles, however, are always determined in the manner illustrated here, even when the forms are more complicated and have correspondingly more points to determine. Always reduce construction to its simplest basic form and then develop any additional details.

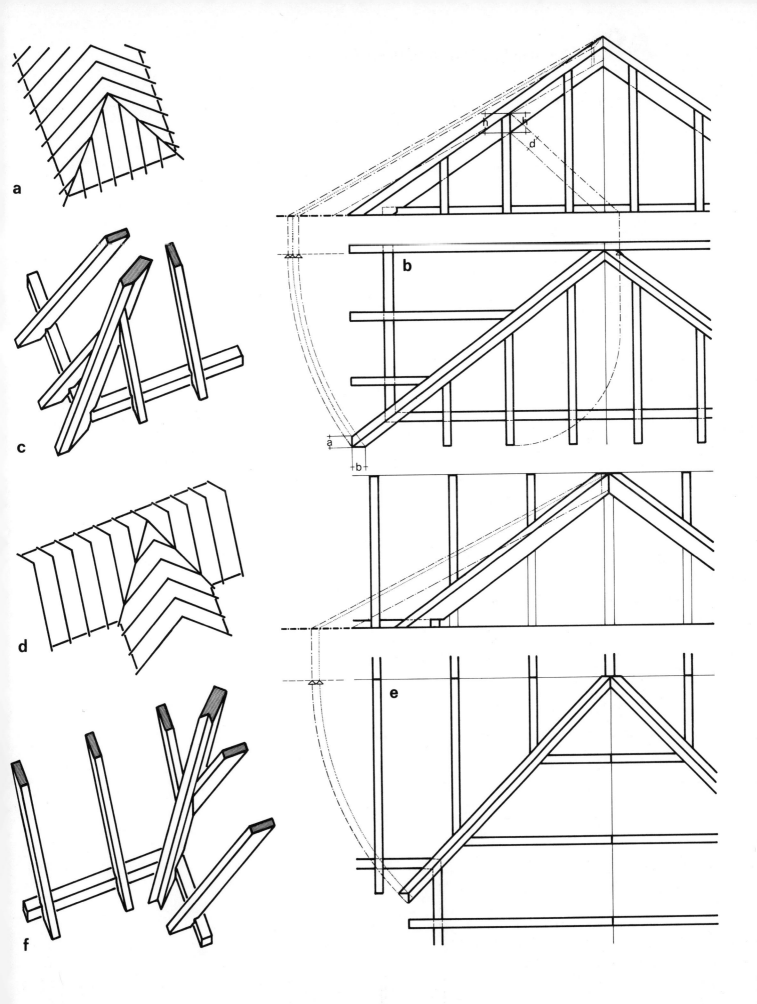

a

c

d

f

b

e

35

A10 Intersection of Simple Bodies

When one object pierces another, they intersect. The pierced object and the piercing areas have a common line of intersection.

All bodies composed of several parts illustrate various forms of intersection.

In a technical illustration, begin with the basic outline form of each individual body and then construct the common line of intersection.

Intersection of Two Pyramids

a Two pyramids over a square plan. In this case, a tall, narrow pyramid pierces a wide, low pyramid. The points of intersection of the pyramids can be determined from the elevation. The intersection of the two pyramids is a straight line.

Intersection of a Pyramid and a Standing Prism

b A square prism pierces a square-based pyramid which is constructed at a 45° angle to the picture plane. In this way, four sections (roof areas) are created, which are cut out of the area of the pyramid. This figure produces the same height dimension for the triangular section (gable) as for the distance from the apex of the triangle (gable apex) to the top of the pyramid (roof top). When these height proportions are changed, a bend is created in the height of the gable top (dot-dash line). The roof areas created by this form are bent, not flat.

Intersection of an Eight-Sided Pyramid and a Standing Prism

c A square prism pierces an eight-sided pyramid. The resultant figure shows four cut triangles (gables). The sides of the pyramid form eight hips: four short ones (those from the tip of the gable) and four long ones (those from the corner of the prism leading to the apex). The horizontal section in the height of the gable ridges (tops) results in a regular octagon. If the height proportions in such a tower change, a bend in the roof area results, as in **b,** above. (Note dot-dash line.)

Intersection of a Four-Sided and an Eight-Sided Pyramid

d A low, four-sided pyramid is pierced by a tall, eight-sided pyramid. The base lines of the eight-sided pyramid which lie parallel to the base lines of the square-based pyramid have horizontal intersection lines. These lines are determined in the elevation and then transferred to the plan. The hips of the four-sided pyramid pierce the four sides of the octagon-based pyramid. In order to find the true height of the points of intersection, the true slope of the hips of the lower pyramid must be drawn. Its point of intersection with the sides of the taller pyramid produces, in elevation, the height of the desired points of intersection. With the height established, the point of intersection of the hip can be drawn in elevation. The line of intersection is then projected from the elevation to the plan.

Intersection of an Irregular Pyramid and an Inclined Plane

e An irregular five-sided pyramid intersects an inclined plane. The points of intersection of the side corners are determined by cutting planes according to A8 **f.** The cutting planes are laid in plan, so that in each case a side of the pyramid lies in one of them. In the elevation, the cutting planes produce the point of intersection of the respective sides.

In another construction, a side view is drawn perpendicular to the direction of the inclined plane. This view produces the height of each individual point of intersection. These heights are then projected to the elevation, **e₁**.

Intersection of Two Prisms

f A standing prism on a square plan is pierced by an irregular four-sided prism inclined to both horizontal and vertical planes. To determine the points and lines of intersection, two cutting planes are laid in the direction of the sides of the standing prism. These planes appear in plan as a straight line and produce the points of intersection of the individual edges (corners) with the standing prism. By projecting the individual points of intersection to the elevation, the exact area intersected is found.

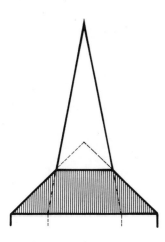

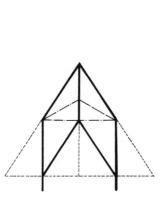

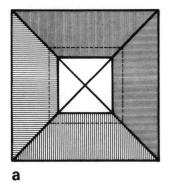

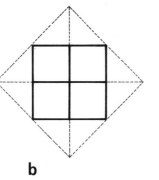

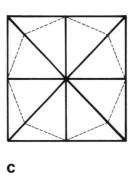

a

b

c

d

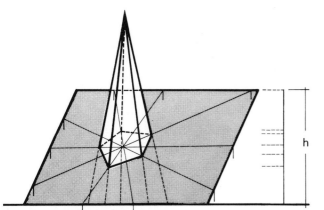

e

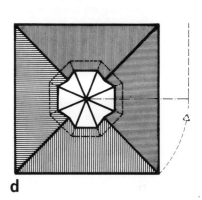

f

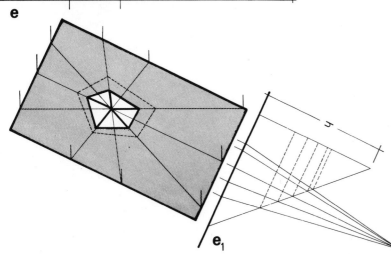

e₁

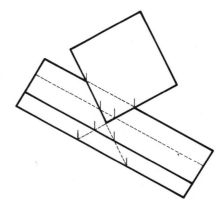

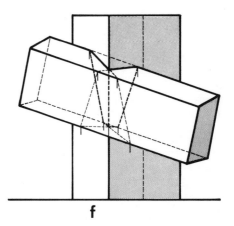

A11 Construction of Shades and Shadows (Orthographic Projection)

Technically, shadow constructions are intersections. They are excellent training aids in spatial perception. Graphically, they offer the possibility of strongly characterizing or accenting the form of an object. Shadows also make a drawing more appealing. Illustrating shadows (by toning or lines) depends upon the kind of drawing (quick sketches, precision renderings, etc.), the drawing material, and the instruments used.

That part of an object which is not reached by light rays from an established light source is said to be in shade. A shadow is caused by the interruption of the light rays that results from the presence of a body between the source of light and the surface on which the shadow falls. Therefore, the outline of a shadow is dependent upon the shade lines of an object.

Shade and Shadows Clarify an Object

a, b Elevation **b** appears more three-dimensional after shadows are drawn in.

c The elevation alone does not describe the plan (compare A3 **b**). The object becomes more readable as soon as the shade is drawn in and its form becomes more clear.

Light Rays as Shadow-Producers

d The characteristics of light rays form the basis for shadow construction. These rays can appear as parallels (as, for example, all shadows generated by the sun).

e The light rays can also emanate from one point (as, for example, all shadow construction based on candlelight or light-bulb rays; see B10).

Shade and Shadow of a Simple Body in Orthographic Projection

f Here is an isometric view of a simple building. Its shadow is found by the given direction of light (R) and the angle of the ray (N). The intersection of these two lines results in the corresponding shadowpoint (P). The dark surfaces on the object itself are shade. The shadow of an object is always projected onto some other surface, in this case the horizontal plane. The shadow forms a silhouette of the shadow-producing object.

Shade and Shadows of Two Simple Objects

g A small object stands behind a large object, with reference to the light source. The shadow of the large object falls in part on the side and top of the small object and in part on the horizontal plane. First the shadows of the large and the small objects are drawn independently of each other on the horizontal plane according to the given or assumed angle and direction of light rays. The shadow of the large object on the side of the small object is produced by the front vertical edge and a part of the top edge. The shadow A_1 of the upper corner A of this vertical edge lies perpendicular above the piercing point of the directional light ray in the bottom edge of the small object. For the construction of the shadow on the small object, select

a point, B, on the top edge of the large object from which a light ray is projected. Perpendicular below the light ray, draw the illustrated triangle on the top of the small object. The point of intersection of the base and the light ray is the desired shadow point, B_1. At the intersection of the shadows of the top right front edge of the large object and the top right rear edge of the small object, lies its shadow point, C_2 (on the horizontal plane). The light ray producing this point strikes the top of the small object at C_1. The shadow on top of the small object can also be found with C_1.

Basic Principles of Shadow Constructions as Intersections

h A point in space which is met by a light ray produces a line of shadow, and produces as its shadow the point of intersection of this line with the plane on which its shadow falls.

i A straight line in space which is intercepted by light rays produces a shadow plane, and then produces as its shadow a straight line in the plane on which the shadow falls.

k A surface in space which is intercepted by light rays produces a shadow object (a body of shadow), and produces as its shadow the intersection of this shadow with the plane on which the shadow falls.

l An object in space which is intercepted by light rays produces a shadow object. Its shadow, on a shadow-receiving surface, is a silhouette of the shade lines of the shadow-producing object.

a

b

c

d

e

f

N

R

P

g

A

B

C

C₁

B₁

A₁

C₂

h

i

k

l

A12 Shadow Construction with the 45° Angle

Shadow construction in the normal plan-elevation system is usually drawn with a 45° light direction in plan and a 45° light angle in all elevations.

The Shadow of a Cube

a A cube in plan and elevation. Shadow at a 45° angle falls entirely on the horizontal plane. The shadow corresponds to the silhouette of an oblique view of the cube (dark shading). If the object in the same plan is increased in height (drawn lightly in elevation), a part of its shadow falls in the frontal plane (light shading).

Light Rays at a 45° Angle

b The light rays appear in the front elevation, side view, and plan at the same angle, 45°, corresponding to the surface diagonals of the cube. The true angle of the light ray in space corresponds to the diagonal of the cube as a three-dimensional body. It is found by rotating, as illustrated in **b**. The angle to the horizontal is smaller than 45° —it amounts to 35°16′.

c Oblique view of the light ray angle and of the true light ray as the diagonal of the cube.

Shadow of a Cantilevered Deck

d Pictorial view of a cantilevered deck extended beyond a wall. The shadow of the cantilevered deck falls on the vertical wall and is determined by the direction and angle of the light ray. Both the direction and angle of light are drawn in an auxiliary plane, which cuts the wall vertically in the direction of the light ray. The line of intersection of the auxiliary plane with the wall and the angle of light produces a shadow point. All shadow points of the deck's front edge lie at the same height. The shadow of the lower left edge of the cantilevered deck runs from the endpoint of the shadow of the front edge, E, up to the point where the lower left edge of the deck intersects the wall.

Illustration of a Transparent Plane

The auxiliary plane in the direction of the light ray is also drawn here as an example of the illustration of a transparent surface. Such illustrations are necessary with the use of glass.

e The same cantilevered deck as in **d,** above, in front and side elevations. The side elevation shows the height of the shadow projected at an angle of 45°, and the front elevation reveals the boundary of this shadow line, to the left. Construction of light rays at an angle of 45° has the advantage that the distance from the shadow-producing line to the plane on which the shadow falls is the same as the depth or height of the shadow, with reference to plan and elevation respectively. The distance the deck cantilevers out from the wall is also the distance for the shadow height on the house wall, starting from the underside of the deck.

Shadow of a Cantilevered Deck on Two Planes

f A simple door niche (recess) with three steps in front and a trapezoidal deck above. The shadow of the cantilevered deck falls on two planes. This is important for the shadow construction of the left corner and the left side of the deck.

The shadow is constructed point by point. First construct the shadow of E, E_1 on the house-wall plane. The connection of this shadow point with the intersection of the left edge of the deck and the house wall produces the shadow of the lower left edge of the cantilevered deck on the outer wall. Then determine the shadow of point E, E_2 on the recessed door. From this point the shadow of the deck's left edge on the recessed roof opening runs parallel to the shadow which falls on the house wall.

According to another system, one may first draw the shadow of the point E on the surface of the door. Then extend the left side of the cantilevered deck to the door plane (dotted line). The connection of the shadow point E_2 with the intersection of the deck and the door plane A produces the shadow of the deck's left edge on the door. Draw the shadow of the edge on the house wall, parallel to it.

Shadows on an Inclined Plane

g The shadow of a dormer can be constructed from the side and front views by drawing the 45° lines, point by point, in both views. The heights of the shadow points are revealed in the side view.

The construction, however, can also be executed in the plan and front elevation views by constructing cutting planes at an angle of 45° through the shadow-producing points in plan. The lines of intersection of these cutting planes, together with the shadow projection of the pertinent points in the front view on the roof surface, produce the shadow points. The construction corresponds to A10 **e.**

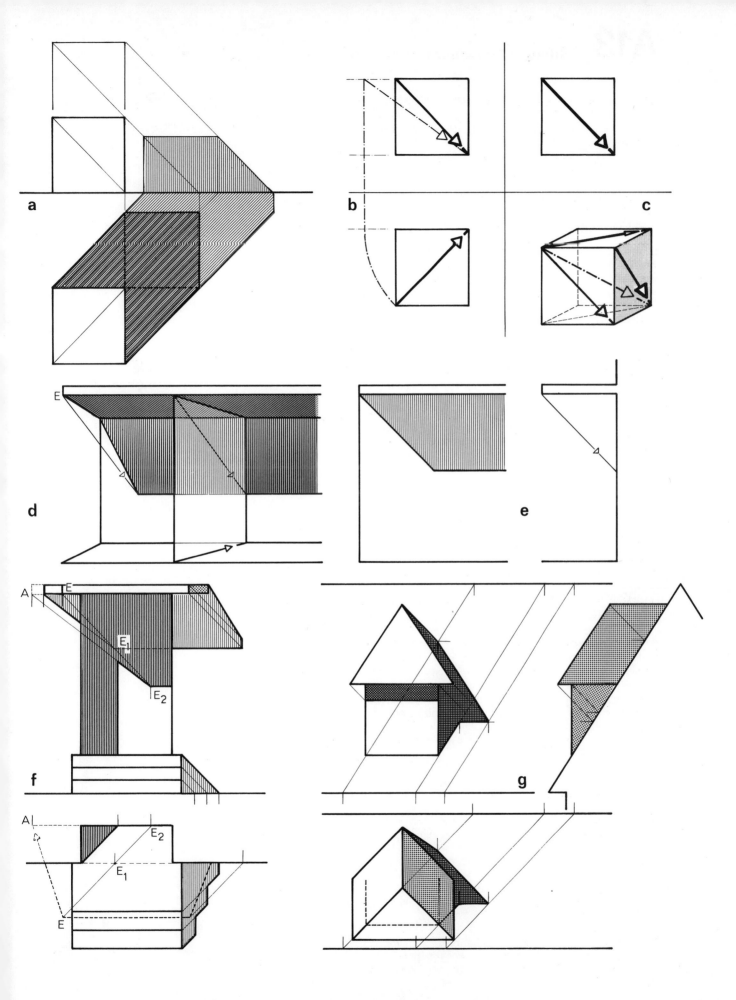

a

b

c

d

e

f

E
A
E₁
E₂

A
E₂
E₁
E

g

A13 Shadow Projections of a Circle

The Circle Produces a Shadow Cylinder

a A circle which is intercepted by light rays produces a shadow cylinder. The shadow appears as a section of this cylinder on the plane on which the shadow falls.

Shadow of a Circle in the Horizontal Plane

b A circle in plan and elevation—the surface of the circle is parallel to the frontal plane, and its vertical axis perpendicular to the horizontal plane. In this case, all shadow points fall in the horizontal plane. The eight main points of the circle are drawn in, in the 45° direction, as shadow points. The shadow projection in the horizontal plane is an ellipse. For very exact drawings, more points may be plotted or the ellipse can be drawn, as in A14 **i.**

Shadow of a Circle in the Frontal Plane

c A circle in plan and elevation, with the surface of the circle parallel to the frontal plane, and its vertical axis perpendicular to the horizontal plane. The shadow of the circle falls on the frontal plane; thus, the shadow projection is another circle. The shadow is constructed by using a light ray of 45°, in which the shadow point of the center of the circle is determined.

Shadow of a Cylinder

d A standing cylinder in plan and elevation. To begin, the light rays (at a 45° angle, in plan) are drawn as tangents to the top of the cylinder. On the cylinder, they produce the boundary of the shade, which is projected to the elevation. They also produce the side boundaries of the shadow in plan. The circular deck of the cylinder casts its entire shadow in the horizontal plane, and can be drawn by determining its midpoint, corresponding to **c,** above.
If the cylinder were taller (drawn lightly in elevation) a part of its shadow would fall in the frontal plane. The same thing would happen if the cylinder were moved nearer the picture plane. The shadow is constructed point by point, with, of course, a separate construction for that part of the circle which casts its shadow on the horizontal plane, as well as for that part which casts its shadow in the frontal plane. The construction corresponds to **b** and **c,** above, but is rotated 90°.

Shadow of a Circular Arch

e The shadow of this standing semicircular arch is composed of the shadows of four circles. Draw the shadows of all four circles (only the shadow points of the four semicircles are constructed here). The light rays, as tangents in the elevation, produce four points which determine the shade limits of the top and the bottom of the arch. The shadow projection, in plan, produces four half-ellipses, each making up a part of the shadow boundary.

The boundary of the shade on the arch runs as a horizontal line from the front to the back of its upper surface. This shade line appears in plan as a straight line, indicating the limits of light and shade.

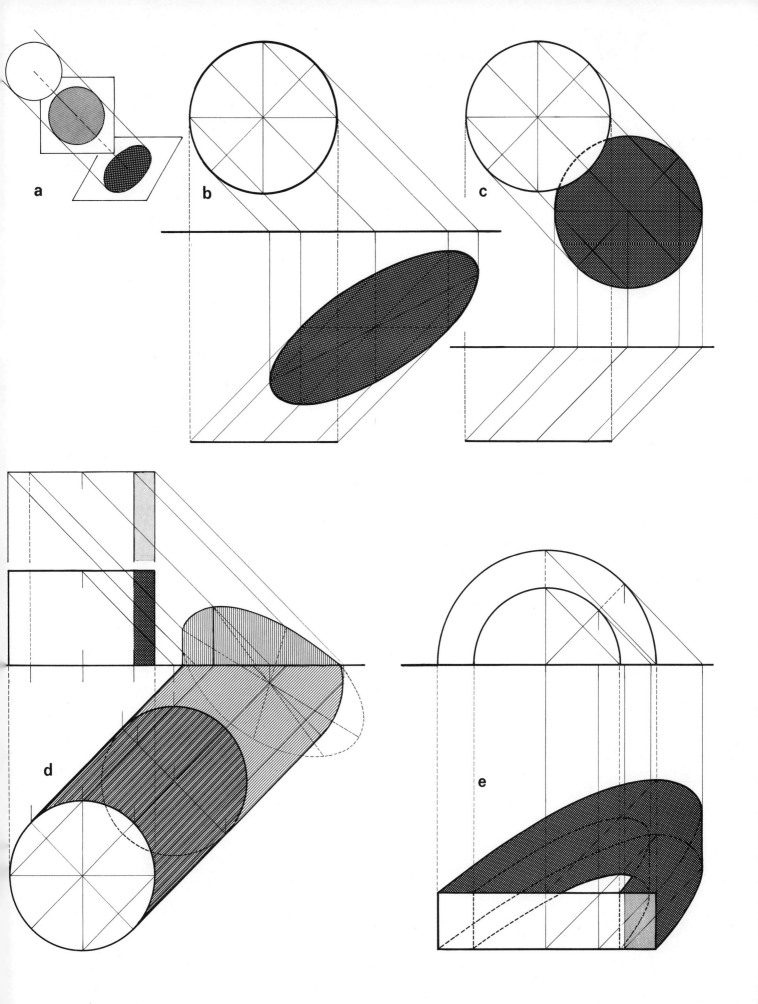

a

b

c

d

e

43

The ellipse is a curve with two symmetrical axes and two fixed points, the focuses. The sum of its distance from any point along the curve to both focuses is constant and equal to the length of the major axis. The focuses lie on the major axis. They are found by drawing an arc with its center at an end of the minor axis and a radius equal to one-half the major axis.

The Ellipse as an Oblique View of a Circle

a If a standing semicircle is rotated in plan, the result in elevation is a half-ellipse, with the vertical diameter of the circle as its major axis and the rotated horizontal diameter as its minor axis. Each tangent to this circle produces, by rotation, a corresponding tangent to the ellipse. These tangents are helpful in the precision drawing of ellipses with a curve template.

Construction of a Circle and an Ellipse Without a Compass

b The circle is a closed curve, all of whose points lie in the same plane and are equidistant from the center. According to this definition, an accurate circle can be drawn without a compass by constructing as many points as are necessary. An oblique view of a circle inscribed in a square shows an ellipse.

Construction of an Ellipse as an Isometric View of a Circle

c An oblique view of a circle inscribed in a square. In an oblique view, the principal diameters of a circle change their relative positions and become conjugate diameters. Conjugate diameters are two diameters of an ellipse which result from the oblique projection of two mutually perpendicular diameters of a circle.

An ellipse is the affined projection of a circle. The connecting line between the center of the ellipse and the center of the circle shows the direction of affinity. Parallels to this direction connect all corresponding points of the circle and the ellipse. The line, about which the inscribed circle and its oblique projection revolve, is the axis of affinity. All lines or cutting planes of the orthographic projection which cross the axis of affinity intersect a corresponding line in the oblique projection. With the aid of the axis of affinity, the main pair of axes of the ellipse is constructed as follows: the midpoint of the circle is connected with the midpoint of the ellipse. Midway on this line a perpendicular is drawn, intersecting the axis of affinity at point M, from which a circle is drawn through the midpoints of the ellipse and the circle. The directions of the main axes of the ellipse are determined from K and G, the points of intersection of the circle with the axis of affinity. The corresponding axes of the circle are drawn, and their intersections on the circle are projected onto the axes of the ellipse in the direction of affinity, thereby establishing the length of these axes.

Mechanical Construction of an Ellipse Using Both Focuses (Gardener's Ellipse, Pin-and-String Method)

d For this construction the focal points of the ellipse must first be determined. To do this cut a piece of string to the length of the major axis. Using one-half the length of the string as the radius, construct an arc from one end of the minor axis. The intersection of this arc with the major axis will establish the focal points. Both ends of the string are then fixed on these points. By stretching the string outward with a pencil or other instrument, the ellipse can be fully drawn in one continuous movement.

The Ellipse as an Elongated Smaller Circle or a Compressed Larger Circle

e An ellipse can be thought of as a compressed or elongated circle. The following construction will clarify this. A small circle, whose diameter is the minor axis of the ellipse, and a larger circle, whose diameter is the major axis, are divided radially into several equal parts. From corresponding points of intersection on the large and small circles, straight lines, parallel to the main axes, are drawn. The intersection of each of these parallel lines produces a point on the ellipse.

The Simplest Ellipse Construction (Trammel Method)

f Beginning at point A, transfer onto a strip of paper one-half the large axis AC and, in the same direction, one-half the small axis AB. When the strip is moved, keeping B on the major axis and C on the minor axis, A is always a point on the ellipse. In this manner as many points as desired may be easily plotted.

The Ellipse as a Sectional View of a Cylinder

g The section of a cylinder which is cut on a plane oblique to the main axis of the cylinder appears elliptical in shape. The perpendicular main axes of the circle in plan become conjugated diameters of the ellipse.

Development of the Ellipse as a Sectional View of a Cylinder

h Roll out the cylinder on a vertical plane and construct the division lines corresponding to those pre-established in plan. From the elevation of the cylinder, the heights (h_1, h_2, etc.) are transferred to the relative division line of the roll-out (or girth).

Determining the Major Axes of an Ellipse from a Pair of Conjugate Diameters (Construction According to Rytz)

i The end of a conjugate diameter, A, is rotated 90° in plan. Connect this point (A) with the end point of the nearest conjugate diameter B by a long, straight line. Bisect the distance between the points. From the midpoint, M, construct a circle through the midpoint of the ellipse intersecting the line drawn through (A)MB. Lines from these intersections to the intersection of the conjugate diameters establish the direction of the main axes of the ellipse, with the shorter distance being one-half the minor axis, and the longer distance one-half the major axis.

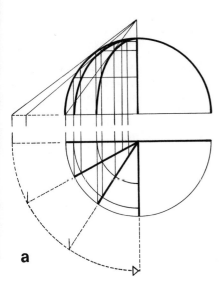

a

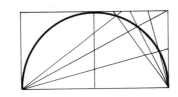

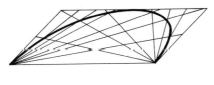

b

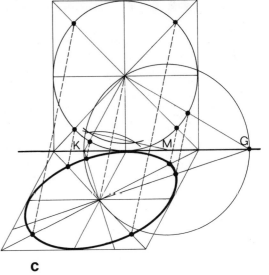

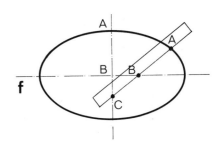

c

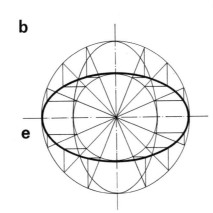

d

e

f

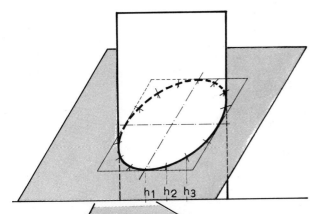

g

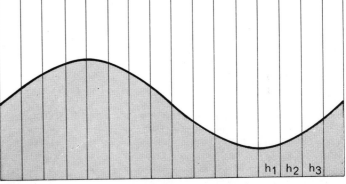

h

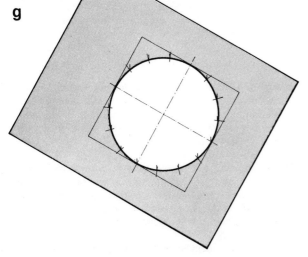

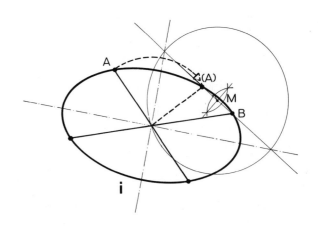

i

45

A15 Polygons and Curves

a An equilateral triangle inscribed in a given circle.
Draw the diameter of a given circle. Using the circle's radius and the intersection of the diameter with the circle as a center, construct an arc which intersects the circle at two points. These are then two points of the desired equilateral triangle. Connect these two points and construct a perpendicular to this line through the center of the circle. The intersection of the perpendicular with the circle is the third point of the equilateral triangle.

b A regular hexagon inscribed in a circle. The length of each side of the hexagon is equal to the radius of the circumscribed circle.

c An inscribed regular hexagon, using the 60° triangle.

d An inscribed regular hexagon, using the 30° triangle.

e A regular pentagon inscribed in a circle. Bisect the radius of the given circle. With this point as a center, draw an arc with a radius of the given circle intersecting the circle and the diameter. The distance between both intersections is the length of one side of the pentagon (heavy dot-dash line). The remaining sides are similarly constructed.

f A regular decagon inscribed in a circle. Draw a regular pentagon as described in **e,** above. Then draw a line from each corner of the pentagon, through the center of the circle, to the opposite side of the circle. The new intersections thus obtained are the remaining corners of the decagon.

g A regular octagon inscribed in a square. From each corner of the square, construct an arc with radius equal to one-half the diagonal. Connect the eight points of intersection with the sides of the square.

h A regular septagon inscribed in a circle. With point A on the circle as center, and with the radius equal to the radius of the given circle, construct an arc intersecting the circle at two points, B and C. Connect B and C with a straight line, intersecting the perpendicular diameter at D. BD and DC are the length of the sides of the desired septagon.

i A regular nonagon inscribed in a circle. Divide the vertical diameter into nine equal parts. With both end points as centers, and the diameter of the circle as the radius, construct intersecting arcs. From these intersections draw straight lines through points 2, 4, 6, and 8. The intersection of these lines with the circle produces the eight desired points; the starting point is the ninth.

k Approximate spiral. As a base figure, draw a small square with extended sides. With one of the corners as the center, and the radius equal to one side of the square, draw an arc terminating at the next extended side. With the next corner as the center, and the radius increased by the length of one side, draw another arc. Repeat this process until the desired spiral is achieved. Such a spiral can be drawn about any regular polygon; the more sides the polygon has, the more gradual the spiral. The perimeter of the base polygon, in this case the square, is the distance between spirals.

l A regular spiral (spiral of Archimedes). The spiral of Archimedes is the plane curve generated by a point moving uniformly along a straight line which revolves about a fixed point with constant angular velocity.

With intersecting diameters, divide an imaginary circle into a number of equal parts. The distance between turns, AB, is divided into as many parts as there are radii (16 illustrated). Starting at the center, the first point lies on the first radius at a distance of $\frac{1}{16}$ AB, the second point lies on the next radius in the same direction, $\frac{2}{16}$ AB from the center, and so on. The constructed points are connected in a smooth curve. The spiral may be drawn clockwise or counterclockwise.

Spirals are especially important in mechanical engineering —in the construction of gear systems, for example. Although they are used much less in building construction, they may be required in certain details of steel or reinforced concrete forms.

m Involute of a circle. The involute is a spiral curve traced by a point on a taut, flexible thread as it is wound upon (or unwound from) another curve (e.g., the end of a taut thread as it is wound about a standing spool). To draw the involute, divide a circle into a desired number of equal parts. Construct tangents to the resulting points along the circumference and transfer onto each tangent the length of the arc from the point of beginning to the respective point of tangency. The involute is completed by connecting these points in a smooth curve.

n A cycloid. A cycloid is the curve generated by the motion of a point on the circumference of a circle rolled in a plane along a straight line. For the construction of the curve, divide the rolling circle into a number of equal parts, then draw a tangent to the base of the rolling circle. Make the tangent the length of the circumference of the circle. Divide the tangent into the same number of equal parts as the circle; then transfer to a perpendicular, from each division point, the height of its corresponding division point on the circle. Connect the resulting points with a smooth curve to complete the cycloidal curve.

o A hypocycloid. The point of a circle which rolls within another circle describes a hypocycloid. The construction is similar to **n,** above, but develops along a curved base instead of on a straight line.

p An epicycloid. The point of a circle which rolls outside and along the circumference of another circle describes an epicycloid. Construction is similar to **n,** above, but develops along a curved base instead of on a straight line.

q Tangents to a curve from a point outside the curve. From the given point, draw a number of cutting planes and determine the center of each chord. Connect each chord center with a smooth curve. This curve intersects the arc at the point of tangency.

r Perpendiculars to a curve from a point outside the curve. About the given point, draw a number of circles which intersect the arc. Draw the chords and connect their midpoints with a curve. This curve intersects the arc at the other end point of the desired perpendicular.

[**Note:** Spirals are used quite frequently in modern architecture and their construction on paper is, therefore, important to master.]

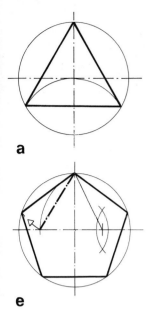

a

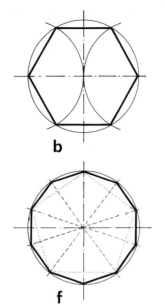

b

60°

c

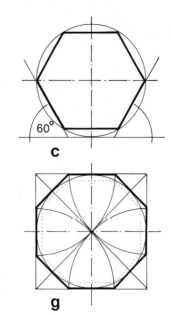

30°

d

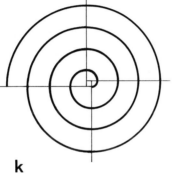

e

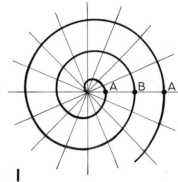

f

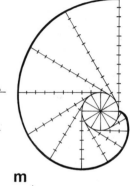

g

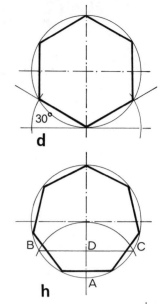

B   D   C

A

h

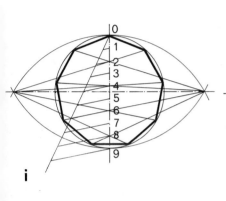

0
1
2
3
4
5
6
7
8
9

i

k

A   B   A

l

m

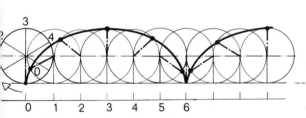

3

4

2

0

0 1 2 3 4 5 6

n

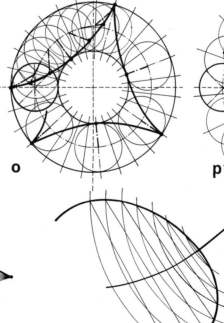

o

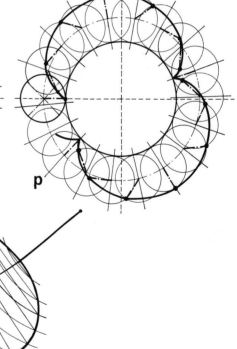

p

q

r

B. The Perspective Drawing

B The Perspective Drawing

The perspective drawing is the technical drawing in which a view of an object is illustrated as it would appear to the eye from a given standpoint. Perspective is a discovery of the Renaissance. To follow its development by Albrecht Dürer or Leonardo da Vinci is a provocative study. However, within the framework of a text on drawing, only its principles must be discussed.

The following section shows all of the possibilities of perspective drawing and the limits of exactness within the perspective. Although it is possible to complete a rendering which very nearly resembles a photograph, it is not very practical to do one if the object can be photographed. On the other hand, a perspective of a planned building can be quite important.

The perspective is often used to sketch ideas, as a basis for the rendering of buildings, or for the presentation of spatial and architectural relationships. The perspective is the best way to show a new building and its environs, or to show a large new building complex as it will appear in or affect the cityscape. Therefore, the use of perspective extends from the drawing of a piece of furniture to the drawing of a complete city.

Several examples of architectural renderings are illustrated:
1 Perspective of the Berlin Playhouse, 1820; a design rendering by Schinkel.
2 Photograph of the same playhouse (1, above), 1935, taken from the identical position as the perspective rendering.
3 Office building for Baltimore, Maryland, by architect Ludwig Mies van der Rohe, 1961. This delineation by Helmut Jacoby is an example of great precision and perfection in drawing technology.
4 Freehand idea sketch of the Einstein Tower, Potsdam, 1920; drawn by Erich Mendelsohn.

[**Note:** A very interesting book to supplement the discussion in this book is Jay Doblin's "Perspective: A New System for Designers." It was published in 1956 by Whitney Library of Design and is definitely worth examining. Doblin's system is indeed new, and it is particularly useful to anyone experiencing difficulty with mechanical perspective.]

4

1

2

3

B1 Derivation of the Perspective from the Central Projection

a The basic principle of the perspective is the central projection (see A1 **d**). All projectors (sight rays) stem from one point, point A. The view obtained by central projection is different from that obtained by parallel projection. In perspective, the size of an object changes constantly according to its distance from the plane of projection, called the picture plane.

Image of an Object on a Sheet of Window Glass

In order to draw a perspective of an object as simply as possible, stand a sheet of glass in front of the object and on it draw the outline of the object with a wax crayon, Pentel pen, or similar marker. One prerequisite is that the head be held in one position. The construction of a perspective according to the so-called windowpane method is based on this general concept.

Construction of a Perspective from Plan and Side View (Orthographic or Windowpane Method)

b A pictorial view of a house on the ground (horizontal) plane is shown. In front of it, at station point S, stands a viewer. The station point in elevation, A, lies perpendicular above. We shall call the distance AS the eye level. The picture plane is placed between the house and the viewer. The sight rays from the individual points of the house to the station point A of the viewer produce the house image on the picture plane, in a perspective view. This corresponds to the view of the house through a windowpane. The individual points necessary to complete the image on the picture plane are obtained by constructions in plan and elevation.

c The elevation of the house, together with the picture plane and the station point of the viewer at eye level A. The eye level must be determined for the construction of the perspective; it lies perpendicular to the station point, S, in the plan. The sight rays to point A produce the necessary height dimensions for the perspective.

d Behind the picture plane is the rotated house plan, in front of it the station point S. Sight rays to this station point produce width dimensions for the perspective.

e The height and width dimensions obtained in **c** and **d**, above, are transferred to a new construction producing the perspective of the house. The considerations outlined in **b** through **d**, above, have played an important role in the development of the perspective. However, the construction, according to this method, is time-consuming, as each individual point must be determined in both plan and elevation. The methods which follow are more practical, eliminating one step (the transferring of height dimensions) by the use of two vanishing points in the perspective drawing.

Vanishing Points

In perspective, lines that are in reality parallel draw uniformly closer as their distance from the viewer increases. These lines meet in a point at infinity, the vanishing point. All parallels in the same direction meet at the same vanishing point. Excluded are the lines that run parallel to the picture plane; these lines remain parallel in the perspective.

Determining the Vanishing Points

f Two areas are subdivided equally in plan and are so constructed that their common corner lies in the picture plane. A sight ray from station point S is drawn, in the same direction as line L, until it crosses the picture plane at VP₁. In the perspective, VP₁ is projected at eye level onto a horizontal line (called the horizon line), thus becoming the vanishing point for all lines parallel to the sight ray from which VP₁ was determined. VP₂ is correspondingly determined by a sight ray parallel to line R. The perspectives of the subdivisions are determined by constructing sight rays from each subdivision to the station point S. The intersection of these sight rays with the picture plane establishes the width of the subdivisions in perspective.

Fundamental Concepts of Perspectives

Vanishing. Objects near the viewer appear large, those far away appear small; that is, the farther they are from the viewer, the more they vanish, and the more difficult it becomes to distinguish details. For example, the profile and hardware are discernible on a window that is near; in the immediate distance, the window divisions can still be seen; far away, only the window opening is visible.

The size of an object. Only the dimensions in the picture plane are to scale. Dimensions behind the picture plane appear smaller than in orthographic projection, those in front appear larger (see A1 **d**, and B1 **a**).

Parallels. Lines which run parallel to the picture plane in the same direction (e.g., all vertical lines in two-point perspective) remain parallel in the perspective. Parallels that are inclined to the picture plane become increasingly close and meet at infinity in a point—the vanishing point.

Position of the vanishing point. All horizontal parallels in nature have their vanishing points at eye level on the horizon. The vanishing points of ascending parallels lie above the horizon; the vanishing points of descending parallels lie below the horizon.

The horizon. The horizon plane is the horizontal plane at the eye level of the viewer. The horizon line is the intersection of the horizon plane and the picture plane.

Color in perspective. Color intensity diminishes as the distance of an object from the viewer increases. The atmosphere lends a bluish tint to colors in the distance. Mountains appear blue in the distance in spite of their greenness in spring and summer or bright variegated hues in autumn. This phenomenon was studied by Leonardo da Vinci; however, it is rarely considered in architectural renderings.

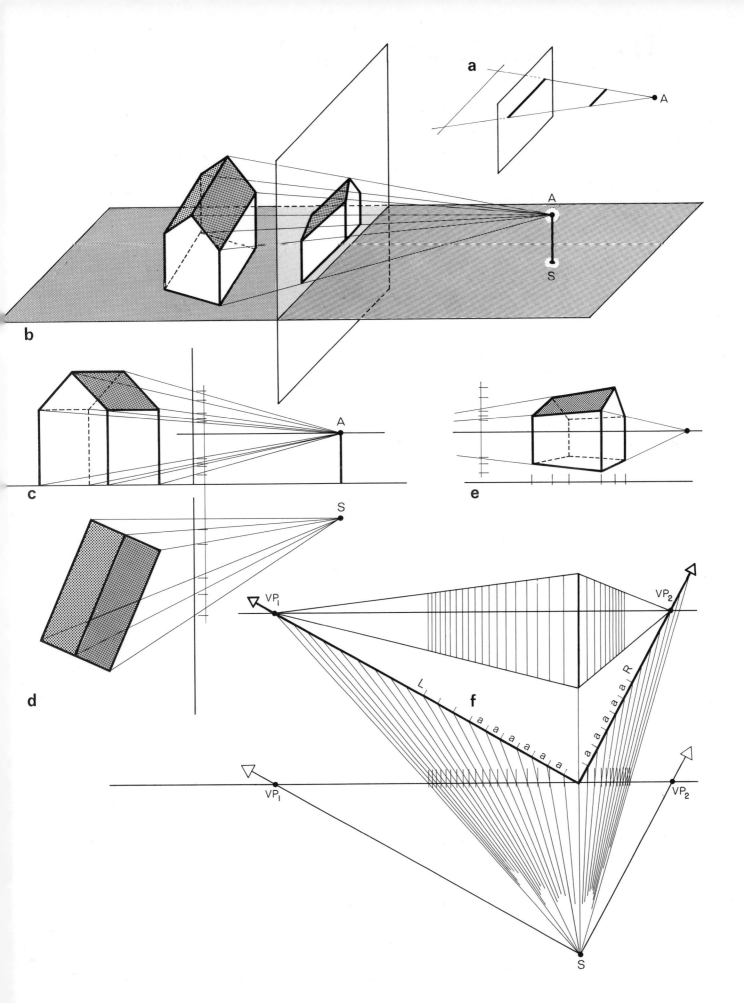

B2 Characteristics of Perspective Constructions

Each perspective has its origin in one of the following three characteristic basic constructions. Before beginning a drawing, one of these constructions must be chosen, no matter whether the drawing is to be an exact construction or a freehand sketch. Each has advantages and disadvantages. The important thing is that the illustration created depict the intention of the planners and the character of the building project, whether or not neighboring buildings and the general atmosphere in which it will be built are included.

Two-Point Perspective

a The body stands perpendicular to the ground plane, with one corner in the picture plane. The sides of the object are inclined to the picture plane. The horizontal lines vanish toward left and right vanishing points. The two-point perspective is most commonly used in the rendering of buildings in natural surroundings or in the cityscape. For construction, see B1, B3, B5, and B7.

Central Perspective (One-Point Perspective)

b The object stands perpendicular to the ground plane, with one side parallel to the picture plane. The front elevation of the object, which lies parallel to the picture plane, appears unchanged (as in orthographic projection). The parallels perpendicular to or inclined to the picture plane meet in vanishing points. The central perspective is most commonly used in rendering interiors and for sketches in perspective. For construction, see B4, B6, and B10.

Three-Point Perspective

c The object stands inclined to the ground plane and to the picture plane. The sides of the object are inclined to the picture plane; horizontal parallels vanish at left and right vanishing points. The picture plane is inclined to the vertical lines of the object; thus, these lines also vanish at a point either below the horizon (as in the illustrated example and B11) or above the horizon (as in B11).

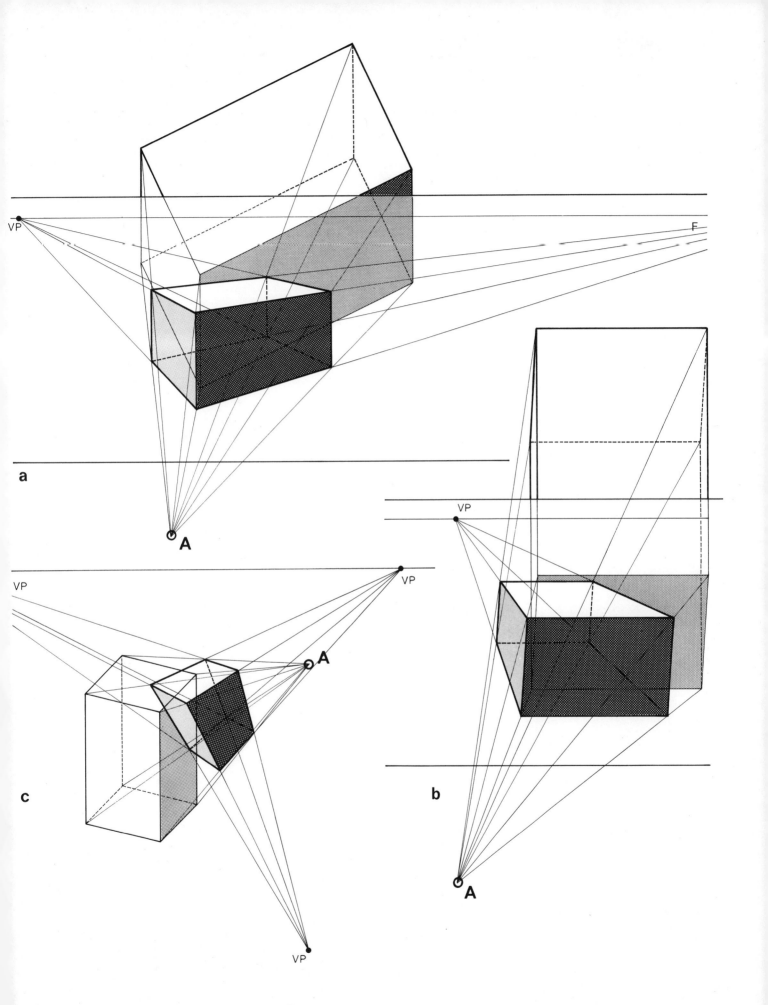

B3 Vanishing Point Perspectives

Two-Point Perspective of a Simple Building with Hip Roof

a Elevation of a simple building with hip roof (geometrically, a cube with a regular four-sided pyramid).

b To construct a perspective, rotate the body in plan and place only its front corner in the picture plane. From the selected station point, determine the vanishing points VP_1, left, and VP_2, right, according to B1 **f.** The left side surface is to be divided vertically into six equal panels. Visual rays from the station point to the panels in plan establish, at their intersections with the picture plane, their relative widths in the perspective (see illustration **c**).

c The panel widths from **b** are projected with thin construction lines. Then the heights are constructed. The front corner, which lies in the picture plane and thus appears in its true height, is divided into six equal parts. The vanishing lines from the top and bottom of the corner to VP_1 and VP_2 produce the upper and lower edges of the cube in perspective, and, correspondingly, the horizontal lines of the right side are constructed.

To determine the height of the roof peak, T, extend the peak to the picture plane in a line parallel to the left side, T_1, and, corresponding to the right side, T_2. Perpendicular above the intersection, project from elevation **a** the true height of the peak, T_1 and T_2 respectively. The vanishing lines from T_1 to VP_1 intersect a perpendicular at T (projected from the picture plane in plan), and thus produce the peak in perspective. The peak can also be found with the vanishing line from T_2 to VP_2.

Two-Point Perspective of a Simple Building with Overhanging Roof

a The overhanging roof is shown in elevation by a broken line.

d Rotated in plan, as in **b,** above, the overhanging roof intersects the picture plane. The triangular section appears in **e** in true size (dot-dash line). Construction of the panels, as in **b,** above.

e Construction of the height, as in **c,** above.

Determining a Vanishing Point Above the Horizon

f Side elevation of a building with a shed roof.

g Plan of a building inclined to the picture plane, with a front corner in the picture plane. Vanishing points VP_1 and VP_2 and the limits of the sides in perspective are determined from the fixed station point.

h Construction of the perspective, as in **c,** above. The side edges of the shed roof are inclined parallels. They can be determined in the perspective by the construction of the corners of the building. Their vanishing point, VP_3, lies perpendicular above VP_1 and is found as follows:
In plan, the inclined parallels run in the direction of vanishing point VP_1. The extended side edges follow the sight rays into infinity (as in B1 **f**), so that the last visual ray has the same angle as the roof pitch, α. From the station point, it pierces the picture plane at this angle, perpendicular above VP_1, and results in VP_3.
The height, h, of VP_3 above VP_1 is obtained by rotation in plan. From the station point, transfer the angle, α, to the vanishing line at VP_1. Erect a perpendicular (broken line) to the vanishing line at VP_1. The hypotenuse from the station point intersects the perpendicular at VP_3, which is the height, h, above VP_1.

Inclined Parallels in the Perspective

In the example, the roof area is divided into equal parts. In perspective, these parallels vanish at VP_3 and are a characteristic example for inclined parallels in perspective drawing.

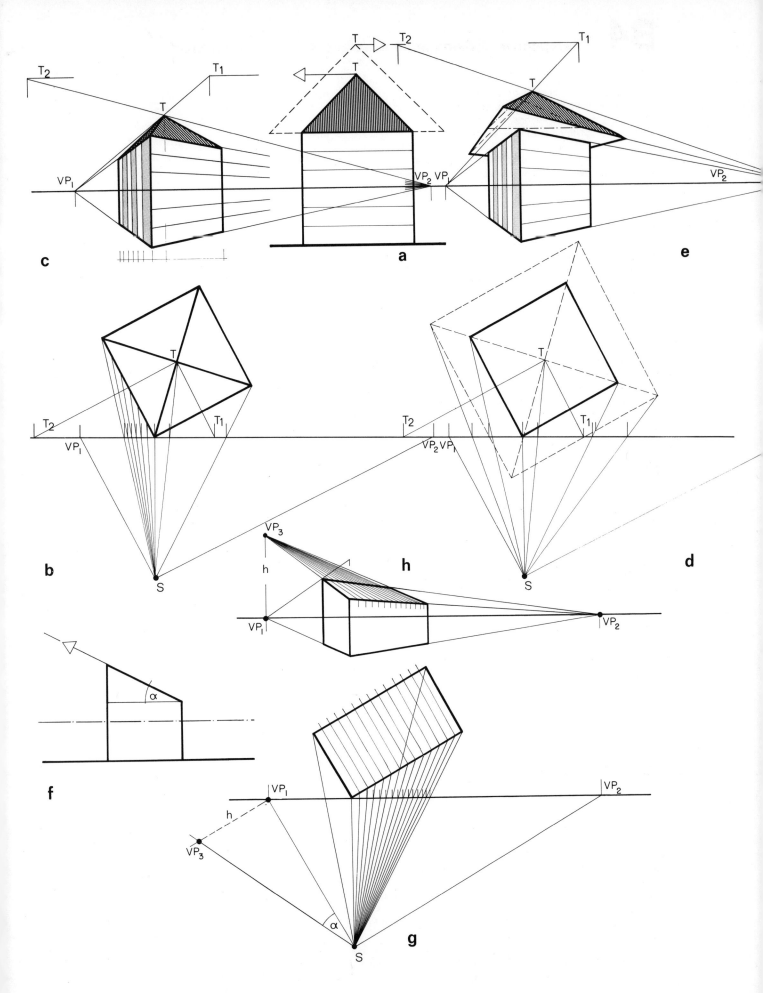

57

B4 Perspective Division of an Area into Areas of Equal Size

The two-point perspective of a row of columns is to be constructed with the vanishing point of the set of lines connecting the base of one column with the top of the next, with all columns equally spaced.

a Elevation of the row of columns with equal spacing. The horizon line and the connecting lines between the base and the top of successive columns (thin diagonals with angle α) are shown.

b The row of columns in plan is inclined to the picture plane. From the station point, vanishing point VP_1 (thin vanishing line) is found parallel to the row of columns. The diagonal connecting lines in illustration **a** have their vanishing point, VP_3, perpendicular above VP_1. Its height above VP_1 is constructed as in B3 **g,** in that the angle α is constructed in plan on the line SVP_1, and a perpendicular to this line from VP_1 is then drawn (height VP_1VP_3, dot-dash line).

c From the plan, transfer the perspective width of the first column (broken line) to the perspective. From the base of the columns, both connecting lines vanish toward VP_3. Their intersection with the upper vanishing line to VP_1 produces the width of the next column. From its base points, determine the next column width, and so on.

Simplified Method for Repetitive Planes in Perspective

d The perspective of repetitive areas of equal size is drawn quickly, as follows. The method is designed for perspective sketches or as a drawing aid for natural appearing perspectives.
Determine the center of the first area by its diagonals or by bisecting a perpendicular. The bisector (dot-dash line) vanishes toward VP. Draw a diagonal from point A (or from the opposite corner below A) through the bisector at the other side of the area, B, down to the bottom vanishing line. The intersection of the diagonal and the vanishing line at point C determines the size of the adjacent area, and so forth. These areas can be further divided perspectively by diagonals (broken lines), both vertically and horizontally. In height, the areas can be divided by vanishing lines to VP.

Practical Illustration of the Simplified Perspective of a Street

e Elevation of the street with building heights, street profile, and horizon line.

f Plan on a module, with picture plane and station point. The module for the houses on the right side is 2, 2, 2, 2 and for the left side is 1, 3, 1, 3. The distance from one side to the other is divided a to e.

g Construction of the perspective (twice as large as the plan, **f**, and the elevation, **e**).
The height and width dimensions of **e** are transferred to the picture plane in double size.
The vanishing point, VP, corresponding to the station point, S, is drawn on the horizon line.
All horizontal lines vanish toward VP.
The spacing is transferred, as in **d**, above; that is, a

bisector to VP is constructed which, when combined with a diagonal, determines the first spacing. Subsequent diagonals, as in **d**, above, determine size of adjacent elevations.

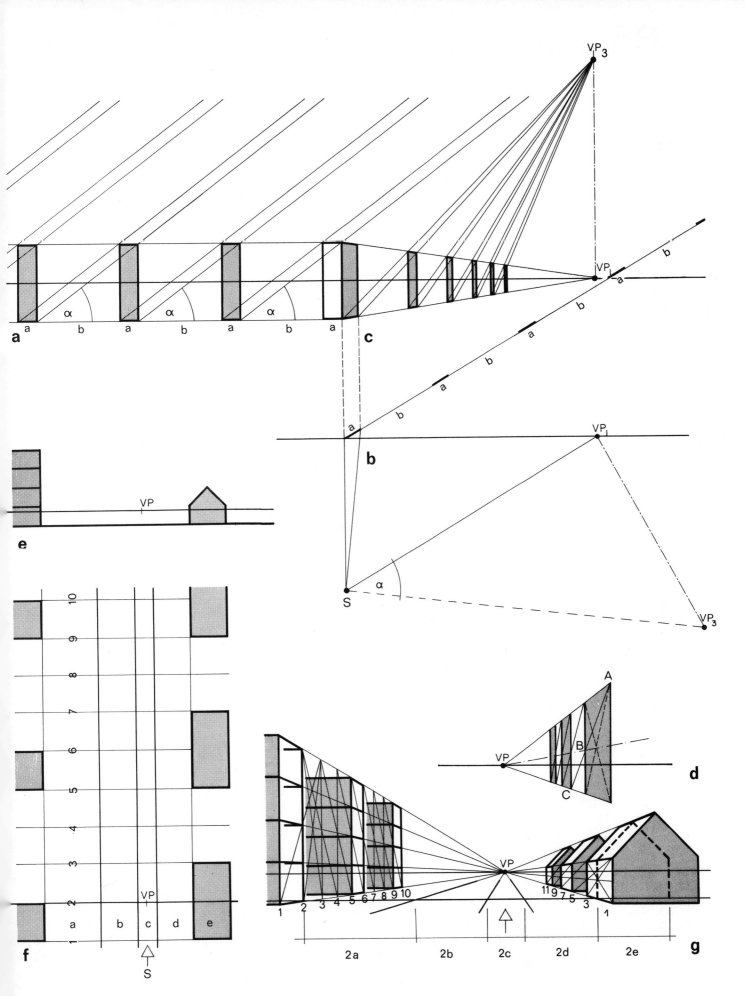

a

b

c

d

e

f

g

59

B5 Two-Point Perspective of a House

a A house in plan and front and side elevations, and given horizon height Ho.

b Construction of the perspective with two vanishing points according to B3 **c.** The plan is placed at such an incline to the picture plane that the typical proportions of the length to the width can be read in the perspective. This means that the gable end should normally appear shorter, and the front, longer. Project vertically to the perspective the front and side dimensions as determined by visual rays in plan. The height dimensions, which appear in true size in the picture plane (front corner), vanish to VP_1 and VP_2.

The paper strip method. It is also possible to mark off on a strip of paper the respective side dimensions as determined in plan and then transfer them to the perspective. This method is recommended in sketching or when plan and perspective must be drawn on different drawing boards.

Basement Perspective

c The basement perspective is sometimes used to avoid the inaccuracies caused by the intersection of lines forming small angles. Since such intersections are often difficult to determine, the perspective is constructed from the usual orthographic plan but, in addition, an auxiliary perspective plan is placed about one story below the perspective. Here a row of columns is shown in plan and inclined to the picture plane with heights given in elevation.

The Dividing Point Method (Measuring Lines)

Once the vanishing lines have been established to the station point S in plan, the intervals along a plane in perspective are most simply constructed with the dividing point method. Project the intervals a and b in plan to the picture plane. The connecting lines between the individual intervals in inclined plan and the corresponding intervals in the picture plane have one vanishing point, T, as parallels. The vanishing lines of the intervals in the picture plane to vanishing point T (dotted line) divide another vanishing line, from the picture plane to VP_2, into the column widths and intervals in perspective (along the front side). The vanishing point of the connecting lines between the intervals in the picture plane and those in the inclined plane is called dividing point T. Care must be taken to ensure that all other vanishing lines of the columns vanish at VP_1 and VP_2. The vanishing lines to T are good only for constructing the intervals of the front surfaces in perspective. The wider apart the columns are, the more distorted are their dimensions in depth. Even the third column no longer appears square, because the field of vision is too large (see B8 **a**).

Perspective Grid (Dividing Point Method)

d The modular dimensions of the grid are drawn in the plan, which is placed at 30°–60° angle to the picture plane, with one corner in the picture plane. Determine vanishing points VP_1 and VP_2 from S by vanishing lines at 30° and 60° respectively. Determine the dividing point T_2 by an arc about VP_1, with the radius VP_1S, and, corre- spondingly, T_1 by an arc about VP_2, with the radius VP_2S. In the perspective, draw the horizon line at its established height, and project vertically on it the vanishing points VP_1 and VP_2 and the dividing points T_1 and T_2. Then transfer the modular dimensions to the picture plane. From each module draw a vanishing line to T_1 or T_2, as appropriate (dotted lines). These divide the vanishing lines AVP_1 and AVP_2 into the modules in perspective. From these modules draw the perspective grid, using vanishing lines to VP_1 and VP_2. Perspective heights above the grid are constructed from heights in the picture plane, as in B3 **c.** The given or assumed height dimensions in this case would be plotted on the front corner and would vanish to VP_1 or VP_2.

[**Note:** A simple grid is very difficult to render in perspective because the squares become distorted at all but the forward corner. One way to diminish the distortion is to experiment with the height of points T_1 and T_2.]

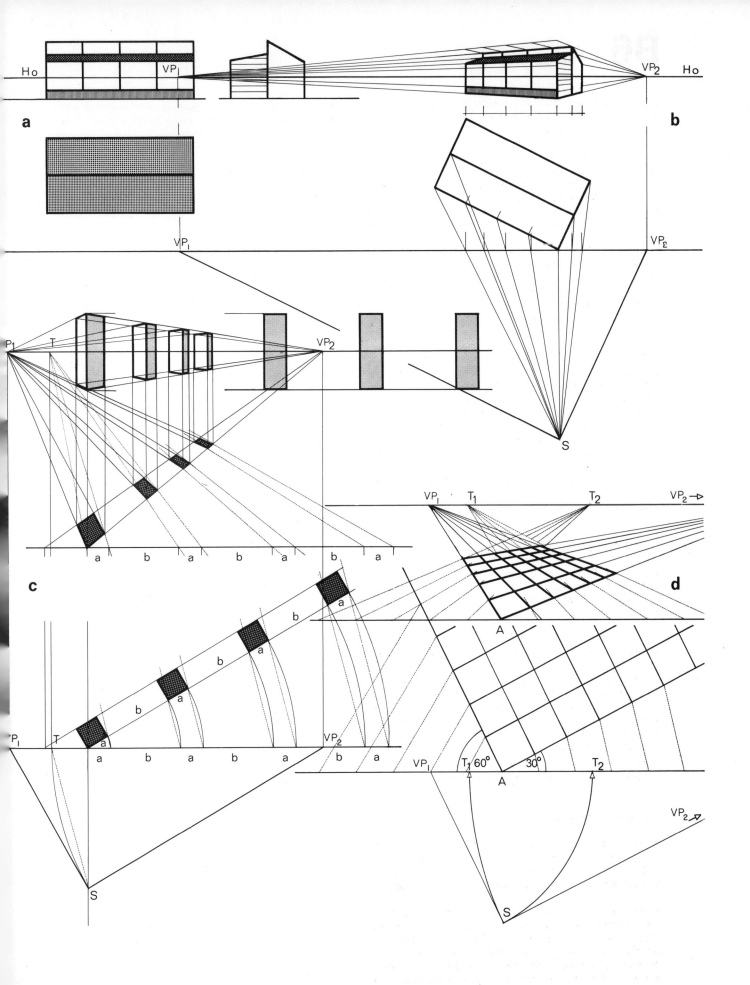

Ho ... VP₁ ... VP₂ ... Ho

a

b

VP₁ ... VP₂

P₁ ... T ... VP₂ ... S

a b a b a b a

c

VP₁ ... T₁ ... T₂ ... VP₂ →

A

P₁ ... T ... VP₂

a b a b a b a

S

d

VP₁ ... T₁ 60° ... 30° ... T₂

A

VP₂ ↗

S

B6 The Central Perspective

If an elevation of a body lies parallel to the picture plane, a perspective can be developed which is especially suited for interiors (see B2 **b**).

a A simple stone bench is placed with its front view (end view) in the picture plane. To the left of the plan, in thin lines, is its side view. The station point S in plan is centered in front of the bench. The perspective is constructed from the front view drawn above the plan. The vanishing point VP lies on the horizon vertically above S. From pertinent points in the front view, draw vanishing lines to VP. The side or depth dimensions are constructed by laying off the individual dimensions in plan (a, b), toward the left from the left-side corner and to the right from the right-side corner. In plan, connect the intervals a and b in the picture plane with their corresponding points on the body. This results in connecting lines (dotted lines) at an angle of 45° to the picture plane. As parallel lines, they have a vanishing point D on the horizon. D is called a distance point because it has the same distance from VP as S has from the picture plane. The construction, shown here in plan, is not necessary for drawing the perspective. Instead, transfer D directly to the elevation, using the established distance from the station point to the picture plane. Next, transfer the dimensions a and b to the left side of the perspective (front view) and draw their vanishing lines to D (dotted lines). The point of intersection with the vanishing line (dot-dash line) from the base of the left-side corner establishes the depth dimension. This view of the object is not too descriptive, since only a view of the front and top can be seen.

Frontal Perspective

b The same bench as in **a.** In order to achieve a better-looking view, the station point S is moved to the left. The construction of this so-called frontal perspective corresponds in general to **a,** above.

Frontal Perspective with Foreshortened Depth Dimensions

c The same bench as in **a** and **b,** above, with front surface still parallel to the picture plane, but at a distance from it. The perspective is carried out as in **b.** However, to save space, the depth dimensions marked on the picture plane are shortened to one-half, as is the dimension VPD. Accordingly, the depth dimension C (from the front surface of the bench to the picture plane) is projected onto the left side of the picture plane at one-half scale.

The Interior Perspective

d Layout of a room interior, plan and wall elevations, at an approximate scale of $\frac{1}{16}'' = 1'0''$. The station point is 19'6" in front of the room, and centered. The eye-level or horizon line (dot-dash line) is approximately 5'0" high.

e For the construction of the perspective, in this case, the elevation is enlarged three times its original size and transferred to the picture plane. However, the depth dimensions are taken directly from the $\frac{1}{16}''$ layout. The distances of all pertinent points from the picture plane are also taken directly from the layout. According to **a,** above, the distance point D is drawn $1\frac{5}{16}''$ to the right of

vanishing point VP. The remaining construction is as in **c,** above, but with depth dimensions at one-third of the scale used in the enlarged elevation.

The Central Perspective Grid

f A table is drawn inclined to the picture plane in plan and elevation, on a grid. The grid module is 20". The table height, 30", corresponds to 1½ modules.

g Central perspective of the grid and the table. The grid is constructed from the modules in the picture plane, whereby the vanishing lines for the widths of the squares are drawn to VP_1, and the vanishing line for the depth dimensions is drawn to D. Transfer the base points of the table legs, corresponding to **f,** to the perspective grid. (These points are obtained by constructing vanishing lines to VP_2 and VP_3 from the picture plane.) The height of the table is determined at any corner by revolving 1½ modules into the respective vertical plane.

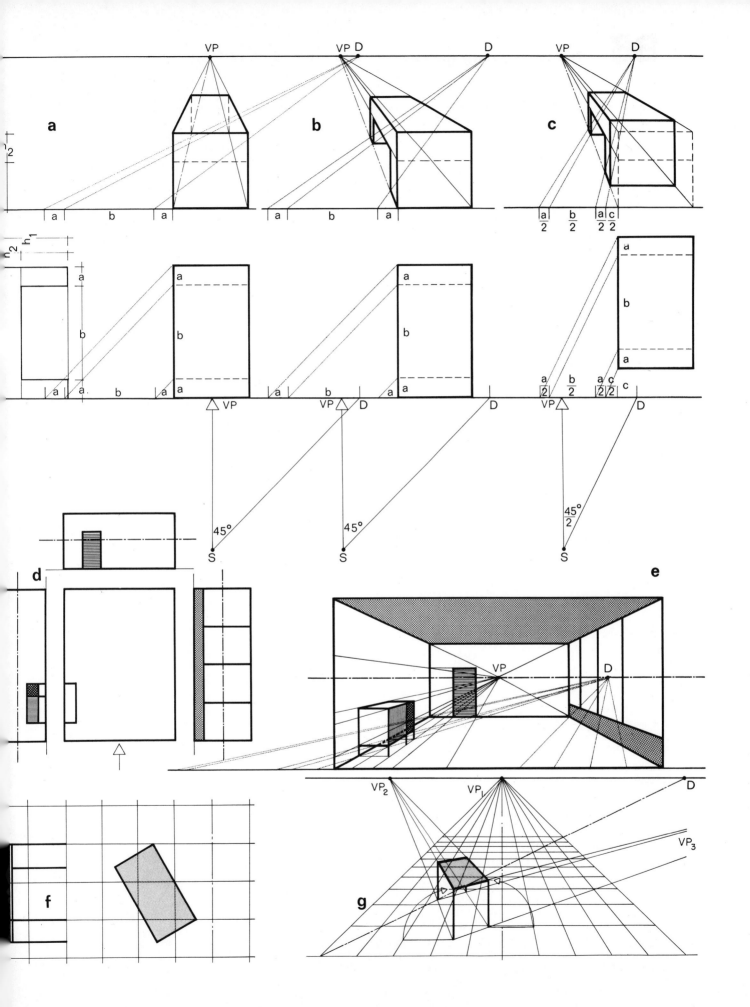

a

b

c

d

e

f

g

B7 The Relationship Between Station Point, Picture Plane, and Perspective

The position of the station point and the picture plane determines the perspective view of an object. Therefore, the station point and the picture plane must be selected with some thought of the desired effect.

Changing the Position of the Picture Plane

a Plan of a house inclined to the picture plane, with station point and vanishing point. Three picture planes (PP_1, PP_2, and PP_3) at different distances from the station point.

a₁ Perspective of the house with picture plane PP_1; a front corner of the house lies in the picture plane.

a₂ Perspective of the house with picture plane PP_2; the house is intersected by the picture plane.

a₃ Perspective of the house with picture plane PP_3; a rear corner of the house lies in the picture plane.

In all three cases, the resulting view is the same. Only the size of the view varies.

Changing the Location of the Station Point to One Side

b Plan of a house, as in **a,** above. In addition, three station points (S_1, S_2, and S_3) at the same distance from the picture plane.

b₁ Perspective of the house from S_1 with a characteristic proportion of gable side to long side (as in **a₁,** above).

b₂ Perspective of the house from S_2. The left gable side appears as a vertical line here because the vanishing line $VP_1 S_2$ is in line with the left side of the house.

b₃ Perspective of the house from S_3. In this case, emphasis is placed on the gable side.

Each movement of the station point to one side or the other creates a different view.

Changing the Distance of the Station Point from the Picture Plane

c Plan of a house, as in **a,** above. In addition, three station points (S_1, S_2, and S_3) at different distances from the picture plane.

c₁ Perspective of the house from S_1 (as in **a₁,** above).

c₂ When the station point is moved very near the picture plane, a highly distorted picture results, although all rules of the construction are adhered to (compare B8 **d**).

c₃ When the station point is moved very far from the picture plane, the vanishing lines become almost horizontal. The question then is whether so much work for such a perspective is worthwhile. In order to achieve a degree of perspective character quickly, consider drawing a rotated elevation with simulated vanishing lines.

The Construction in Perspective of Points in Front of the Picture Plane

A corner of a house with the cornice projected in front of the picture plane.

d₁ Section profile of the corner in order to determine the pertinent heights.

d₂ Rotated plan, with the front corner of the house in the picture plane. Through the cornice, a section view of the cornice can be seen (thin broken lines) as an extension of the wall surfaces. In plan, project visual rays from the station point through the points of intersection of the wall extension and the cornice onto the picture plane. These intervals are transferred to the perspective above at their respective heights in the picture plane, and from these points the cornice sections (shaded areas) are drawn in perspective. The profile lines of the projected cornice in perspective are obtained by drawing vanishing lines through the established points toward VP_1 and VP_2.

d₃ Corner plan as in **d₂**. The cornice section is obtained by transferring from the plan to the perspective the points of intersection with the picture plane. The heights of these points in the picture plane can be plotted to scale in the perspective. Finally, draw the profile lines of the cornice through the corners of the section areas with vanishing lines from VP_1 and VP_2.

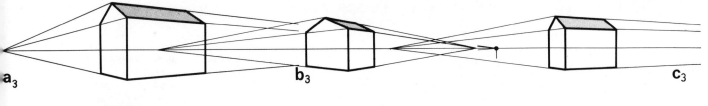

a_3 b_3 c_3

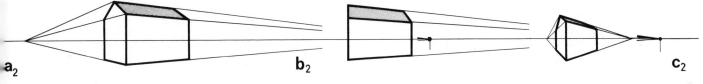

a_2 b_2 c_2

a_1 b_1 c_1

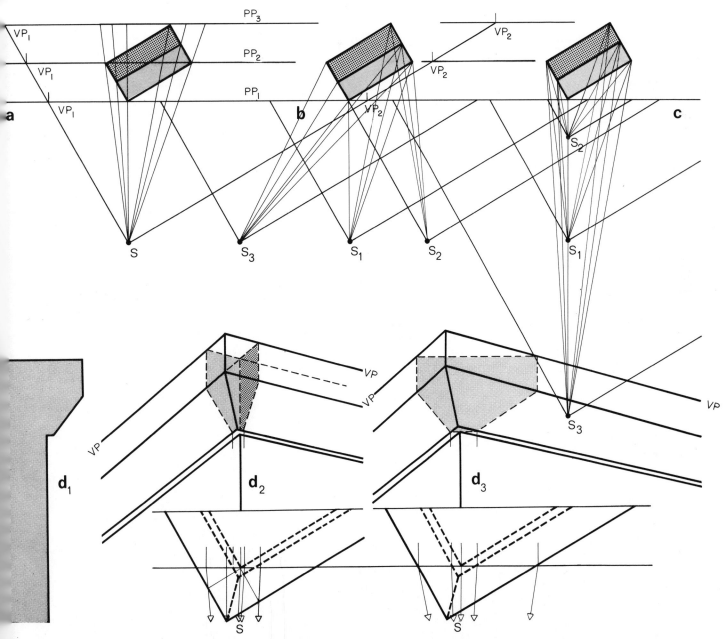

B8   The Limits of Exactness in Perspective

A perspective true in both dimensions and angles can only be drawn on a concave surface when the viewer's standpoint is at its center. If the perspective view is to correspond exactly to that seen in nature, it must be viewed from the center of the concave surface. This is impossible in actual practice. Consequently all perspectives must be viewed from a certain distance range from station point to picture plane, in order to achieve the nearest thing to reality in a perspective view. For example, if the distance from the station point to the picture plane is constructed at six inches, it will be too near the eye.

The Distortion Within the Same Field of Vision

a If one projects equal angles of vision from a station point onto the picture plane, the dimensions they intercept are distorted so that the resulting dimensions gradually increase from the center outward: a, b, c, d, and so on.

b If one lets the angle of vision terminate on a central arc, the intercepted distances, when projected vertically onto the picture plane, gradually decrease from the center outward: a, b, c, d, and so forth.

The Limit of the Field (Angle) of Vision in Perspective

In many perspective constructions (B5 **c**, B7 **c₂**), the field of vision is distorted outward corresponding to **a,** above. To avoid false illustrations due to distortion, the field of vision should not be greater than 50° to 60°. This range corresponds more or less to the field of vision in which our eyes define things clearly.

The Spherical Perspective for Greater Fields of Vision; Correction of the Distortion

c Beginning at the point of tangency of a straight line (picture plane) and a circle, mark off a selected number of intervals, a, in each direction. Vanishing lines from S intercept arc a and are extended to intersect verticals from corresponding points on the straight line. The connection of these points of intersection results in a curve which, as a picture surface, approaches the form of a hollow sphere. In the perspective this counteracts the distortion of the field of vision to a great degree.

d The curve constructed according to **c** may be drawn simply as a circle whose radius is 1.55 times the distance from the station point to the picture plane.

The Perspective on a Curved Surface

e The object to be drawn is placed between the station point S and the picture plane, in plan. Sight rays from the station point through the pertinent points of the object to the curved picture surface produce the depth dimensions in the perspective.

f In the rotated side view, the height of the horizon line (dot-dash line) is fixed. Then, above and below the horizon line, plot the height of each corner of the object at its actual distance from S (measure in plan). The vanishing

lines from A onto the curved picture surface determine the height of points necessary for the perspective construction. The construction of the side view, however, is usually carried out in plan. As a first step, the distance of each corner of the plan is projected by an arc, whose center is S, onto the central sight ray. (Note how the new width dimensions vary from those of the standard side view.) The actual heights above and below the horizon line are rotated 90° in plan, the central sight ray doubling as the horizon line for construction of the side view. Then the heights are projected from S onto the curved picture surface and subsequently transferred to the perspective.

g The resulting perspective (see **e** and **f,** above).

Following the same system, a perspective can also be constructed on a normal picture plane. The perspective originating on a straight line picture plane is drawn in with thin lines. The difference between the perspective illustrations in this case is of little consequence. However, the difference becomes greater as the width of the object increases and as the distance from the object to the station point decreases.

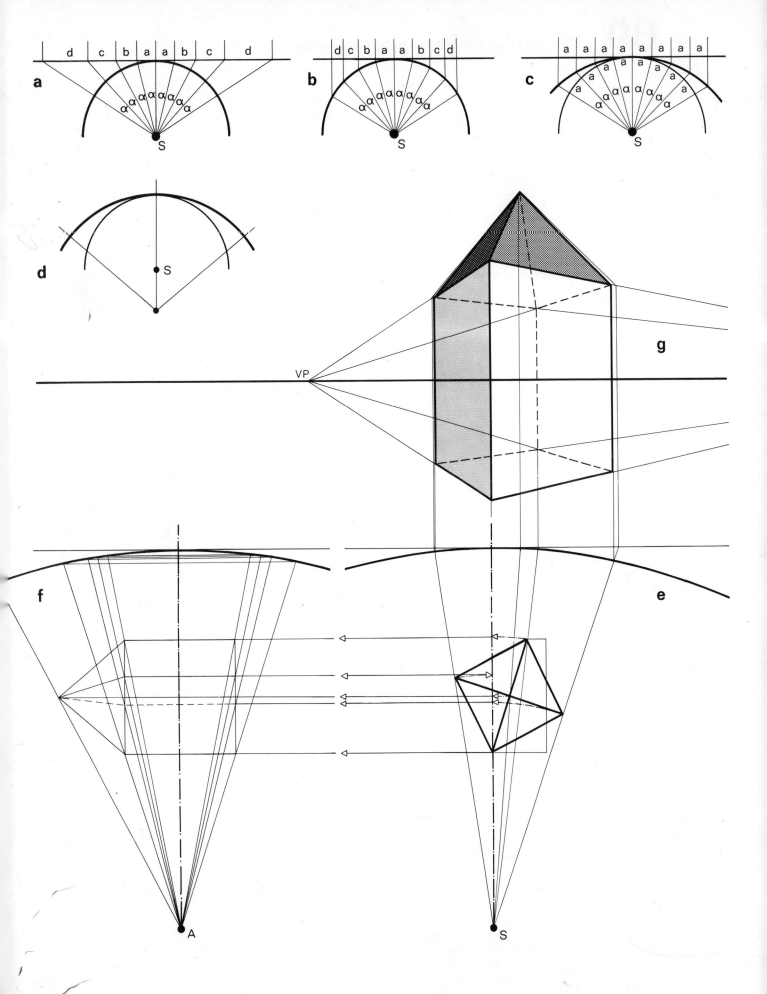

67

The visual rays from the circumference of a circle to the eye form a cone. In the perspective, a circle appears as a conical section, but as a circle only when the section lies parallel to the picture plane and when the central visual ray lies perpendicular to the midpoint of the visible circle.

Varying Perspective of a Circle as a Section of a Cone

a When the station point and the picture plane lie in front of the circle, the circle appears in perspective as an ellipse.

b When the station point and the picture plane lie within the circle, the circle appears in perspective as a hyperbola.

c When the station point lies on the circle and the picture plane is within the circle, the circle appears in perspective as a parabola.

The Circle in Perspective

d A central perspective of a circle inscribed within a square, drawn above and below the elevation. The circle appears as an ellipse (see **a,** above). The major axis of this ellipse is found as follows.

The geometrical center of the square is determined in the perspective by dividing A'A" in half. This center is the midpoint of the desired ellipse. From this midpoint, draw a horizontal line which intersects a side of the square at B'. Extend A"B' (broken line, short strokes) to the axis between the elevation and the perspective. Connect the intersection point of the axis and A"B' with A. This line (broken line, short strokes) intersects the circumscribed square at B. The horizontal through B intersects the circle at C. Draw a straight line from A through C onto the axis between the elevation and the perspective (broken line, long strokes). This intersection with the axis is then connected with A" (broken line, long strokes). At C' this line intersects the horizontal drawn through B'.

Correspondingly, C" is found at the same distance from the midpoint of the desired ellipse. The line C'C" is the conjugated diameter to A'A". Now the ellipse can be constructed according to A14 **i.**

The Sphere in Perspective

The sphere in perspective is always the perspective view of the visible circle, which is formed by visual rays tangent to the sphere.

e A sphere in the side view. The diameter of the visible circle from the station point A is drawn with a broken line. The station point lies at the same height as the midpoint of the sphere; the central sight ray runs perpendicular to the picture plane. Only in this case does the sphere appear as a circle in the perspective.

e₁ When the sphere is moved upward along the picture plane, the visible circle is inclined to the picture plane and its perspective is then an ellipse (see **a,** above). The square circumscribing the visible circle has its vanishing point VP under the horizon line. For construction of the

perspective, the visible circle with circumscribed square is drawn in true size on the connecting line 1-1 (picture plane!). Its vanishing lines to VP intersect the height lines 2-2, 3-3, 4-4. With 2-2 and 4-4, the perspective of the circumscribed square can be determined. The diagonals are found accordingly, and thus the perspective view of the circle can be drawn.

Construction of the Sphere in Perspective (Second Method)

f A sphere in plan on the left, with station point S; in elevation on the right, with eye level h. The points A and B of the major axis of the sphere are, in the perspective, the focuses of an ellipse. On the sphere in plan, the point of tangency T of a sight ray from the station point S is a point of the ellipse in the perspective. The ellipse can be drawn from its focuses and a point on the circumference. From the plan, the horizontal distances between T, A, and B are projected from the picture plane to the perspective. The vanishing point VP is also projected vertically to the horizon line. A, T, and B, as well as the height h for the horizon line, are transferred from the elevation to the perspective. From the points A, B, and T, the ellipse is drawn (see A14 **d**). The position of the major axis of the desired ellipse is determined by the connecting line between the points A and B. Its length corresponds to the dimension AT + BT.

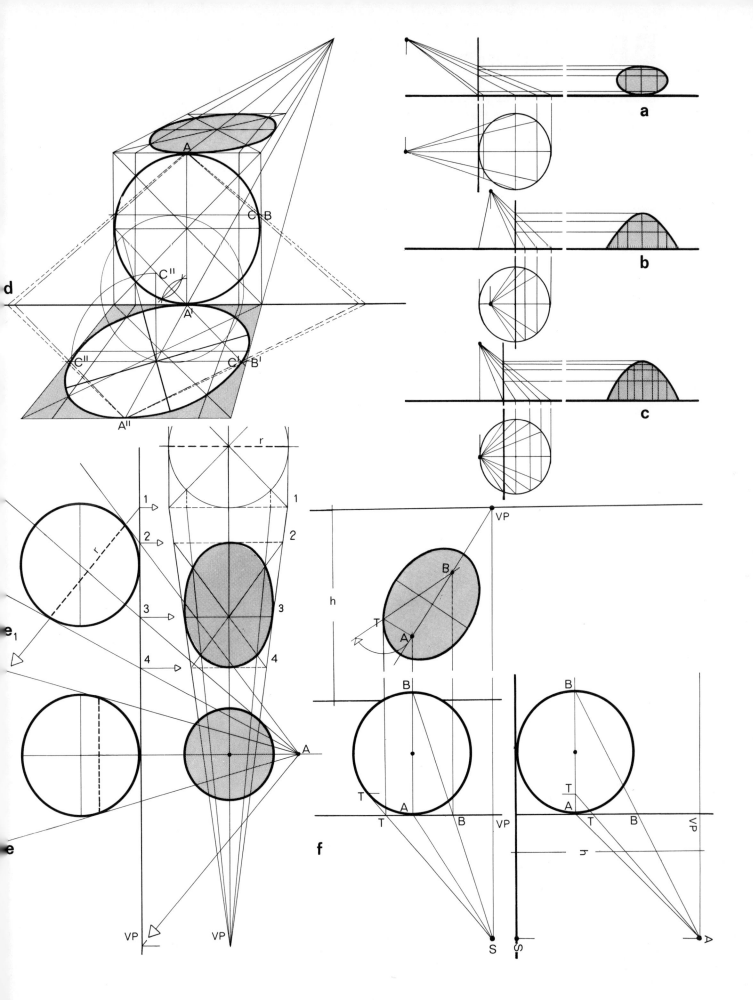

d

a

b

c

e₁

e

f

VP

VP

VP

S

S

69

B10 Shadows in Perspective

To create shadows of an object in perspective, as in nature or photography, there are three possibilities: back-lighting, side lighting, and frontlighting. The shadows are constructed using points according to the same considerations as in orthographic projection (see A11 **f**). In perspective construction, the direction of light and the angle of light are always vanishing lines which intersect in a shadow point. The vanishing lines of the light direction develop from horizontal parallels which indicate the direction of the light in plan. The vanishing lines of the light angle represent the light rays themselves. They are inclined parallels which have their vanishing points above or below the horizon line, according to the position of the light source.

Frontlighting

a₁ The sun is in front of the picture plane, behind the viewer. The vanishing point of the direction of light lies on the horizon line at VPD, while the vanishing point of the angle of light lies perpendicular below at VPA. The intersection of the vanishing lines to VPD and VPA is the shadow point in perspective.

a₂ The same construction as in **a₁**; the direction of light and the angle of light are changed. VPD and VPA remain in place. However, the object itself is moved to the right. Therefore, the shadow appears more to the side, and longer.

Sidelighting

b Here, in relation to the viewer, the sun is so positioned that its rays are projected parallel to the picture plane. In the perspective, the direction of light and the angle of light are parallels. Their points of intersection produce the shadow.

Backlighting

c₁ The sun stands behind the picture plane. All light rays are projected from the sun, which is also the vanishing point VPA for the light rays. The vanishing point VPD for the light direction lies perpendicular below on the horizon line. The intersection of the vanishing lines to VPD and VPA determine the shadow points in perspective.

c₂ The same construction as in **c₁**; the position of the object is changed with relation to the sun.

Point Lighting from One Light Source

d₁ A table in central perspective; lamp to one side. The shadow of a central light source is constructed as in **c₁**. For the light rays, the vanishing point VPA is the light source itself; for the light direction, the vanishing point VPD, in this case, lies perpendicular, below, at the level of the room floor.

d₂ The same table with a lamp on it.

Reflections in Perspective

e The reflection (in the water) of a bridge is to be drawn in a central perspective. In the construction, start with the elevation of the bridge in the picture plane. Then, in this case, the line AA is the height of the water line in elevation. Transfer the height of all individual points above the water line perpendicular below. For example, measure the distance from AA to Bh_1, and mark off the same distance from AA downward (to B_1 in the direction of C_1). Then measure the heights of the remaining parts of the bridge and railing as given from B to C, and mark off each corresponding dimension from B_1 to C_1. These points then determine the reflection of the elevation of the bridge. From the individual points thus established, draw vanishing lines to VP. These intersect perpendiculars from points in the perspective downward and produce further points of the reflection in perspective (e.g., from B_1, the point D_1, not shown but corresponding to D on the bridge, with height h_2). In the reflection in this case, the underside of the bridge appears in a larger field of vision than it does in the perspective of the bridge itself. The shadow of the bridge in backlighting is constructed as illustrated in **c₁**, with the sun as vanishing point VPA and with the vanishing point VPD on the horizon line. Then transfer the shadow points and shadow lines to the reflection.

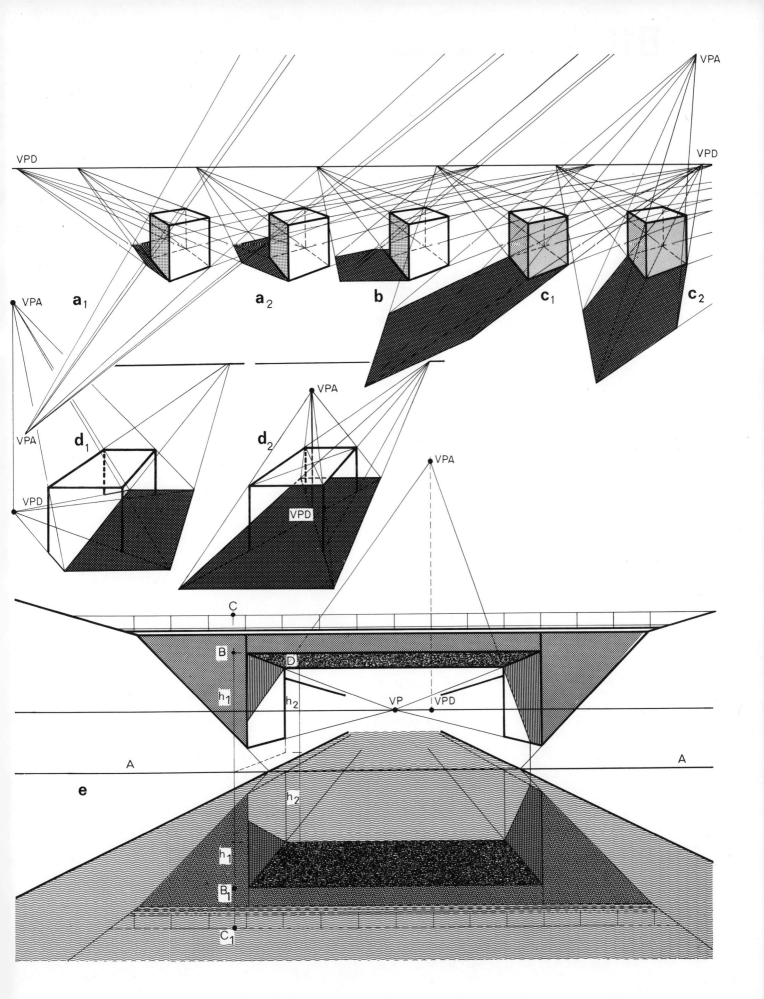

VPA

VPD   VPD

a_1 a_2 b c_1 c_2

VPA

VPA

VPD

d_1 d_2 VPD

VPA

C

B   D   VPA

h_1 h_2 VP   VPD

A   A

e

h_2

h_1

B_1

C_1

71

If an object is viewed through a picture plane which is inclined to the horizontal plane, its vertical lines do not lie parallel to the picture plane, but have a vanishing point above or below the horizon (see B2 **c**).

Three-Point (Bird's-Eye) Perspective

a₁ A body (prism combined with a pyramid) in plan stands inclined to picture plane PP. Its position corresponding to side view **b** is drawn with a broken line in front of the picture plane, so that plan and perspective do not become mixed.

Construction of the perspective. The distance VP₁C between the horizon and the picture plane (intersection of the inclined picture plane with the horizontal plane) is transferred from the side view **b** to the perspective. Draw the main sight ray (dot-dash line). Its point of intersection with the horizon is the vanishing point VP₁ for the depth dimensions in the horizontal plane. The vanishing point VP₃ lies vertically below.

The depth dimensions 1, 2, 3, and 4 of the plan are transferred to PP, and from these points vanishing lines are drawn to VP₁.

b In side view **b,** fix both the inclination of the picture plane VP₁C and the eye level through the station point A₁ (in elevation). The horizontal from A₁ intersects the picture plane at VP₁ and establishes the horizon for the perspective. The vertical from A₁ onto PP produces the vanishing point VP₃ for all vertical lines of the object. VP₃ is transferred to the perspective, retaining the same distance from VP₁.

Draw vanishing lines from the individual points of the object to A₁. These establish the heights for the perspective on the picture plane PP.

From the side view **b,** transfer the height dimensions to the perspective **a₁.** The heights 1 to 4, together with the vanishing lines from 1 to 4, make up the perspective of the square in plan.

Lengthening the vanishing lines from VP₃ through the corner points of the square in perspective produces the vertical corners. Their upper corner points are 1', 2', etc. The roof peak lies above the intersection point of the diagonal of the square. A vanishing point on the horizon can be determined with vanishing lines through the points 1 and 2, and then through 3 and 4 for the left side. These vanishing points serve to control and to complete the construction.

a₂ An alternate view of the same object in three-point perspective. The picture plane is unchanged. The station point in elevation is A₂. Construction is in accordance with **a₁** and **b.**

Three-Point (Frog) Perspective

A frog perspective is created when the eye level and horizon are lower than the object being viewed and the picture plane is inclined to the viewer. As an example, the frog perspective of a cylinder is shown.

c₁ From the plan (as in **a₁,** above) the depth dimensions are determined and the main sight ray fixed.

d The station point in elevation and the inclination of the picture plane are fixed in the side elevation. Here, also, the horizontal from A intersects the picture plane at VP₁ and establishes the horizon line. In this case, the entire perspective lies above the horizon line.

c₂ Alternate three-point perspective of the same object as in **c₁.** The position of the object with relation to the station point has been changed. The perspective is constructed point by point, as in **c₁,** with the same height dimensions from **d.**

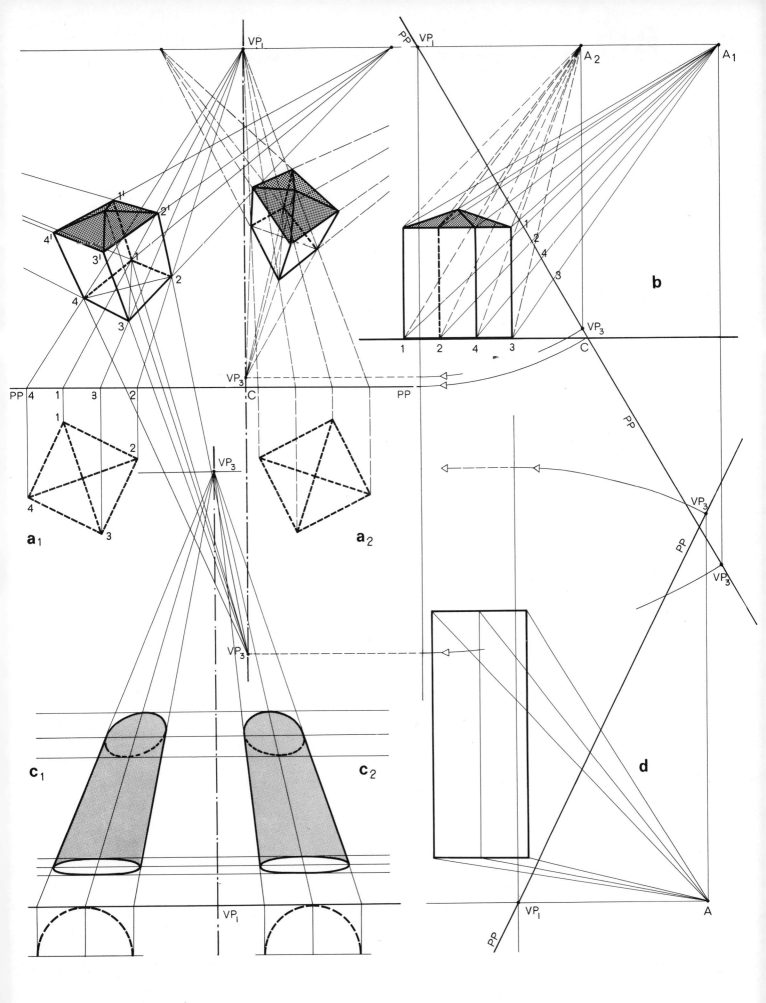

If the human eye is considered solely as a sphere, forgetting individual differences, the outside world is portrayed in the eye as on a hollow sphere. All lines of an object in nature appear as if projected onto this hollow sphere.

a A straight line BC suspended in space is projected through point A on the eye into the eye. It appears as a segment of a circle and is rotated 180° (C above, B below). For illustration here, a plane is drawn from the straight line through the main axis of the sphere and cuts out a circle from it. This circle, inclined to the picture plane, appears as a vertical ellipse. The vanishing lines from B and C through A determine the length of the segment of the circle.

b Plan and elevation of the line BC and DE are portrayed here as straight lines because they go through the picture's midpoint A. In any other position, a straight line becomes an ellipse segment (see **c** and **d**).
All straight lines through the picture's midpoint remain straight; all other straight lines become ellipse segments.

c A hollow sphere in plan and elevation. In the elevation a rectangle is drawn and projected onto the sphere. The sides of the rectangle are thus transformed into circle segments, which appear as ellipse segments in elevation. The corners shift their positions in the projection toward the center (e.g., A to A_1) and the side centers toward the edge (e.g., B to B_1).

d A hollow sphere in elevation behind a square modular grid. Its projection in the hollow sphere is drawn in heavy lines. The circular segments of the sides of the individual modules are complemented according to **a,** above, in both directions, and develop into entire circles which appear as ellipses.
It can be determined that the curvature of the sides of the modules, in the range of the normal angle of sight of about 50° (light area), is not so large that it must be considered in a perspective illustration. One reason is that the elevation of the module is not the actual picture which would appear on the background of the eye, but its projection onto a plane surface. Purely geometrically we know what appears on the inside of the eye, but it is not possible to illustrate this in a drawing on a plane. Technically, physiological and psychological factors would still have to be considered.
The architect will, in most cases, use the constructions in B3 through B7 for his perspectives. He will first decide whether an illustration according to B2 **a** or B2 **b** suits his purpose, and then make the drawing. His perspective should be correct and convincing, well drawn but not misleading; in short, as realistic as possible.

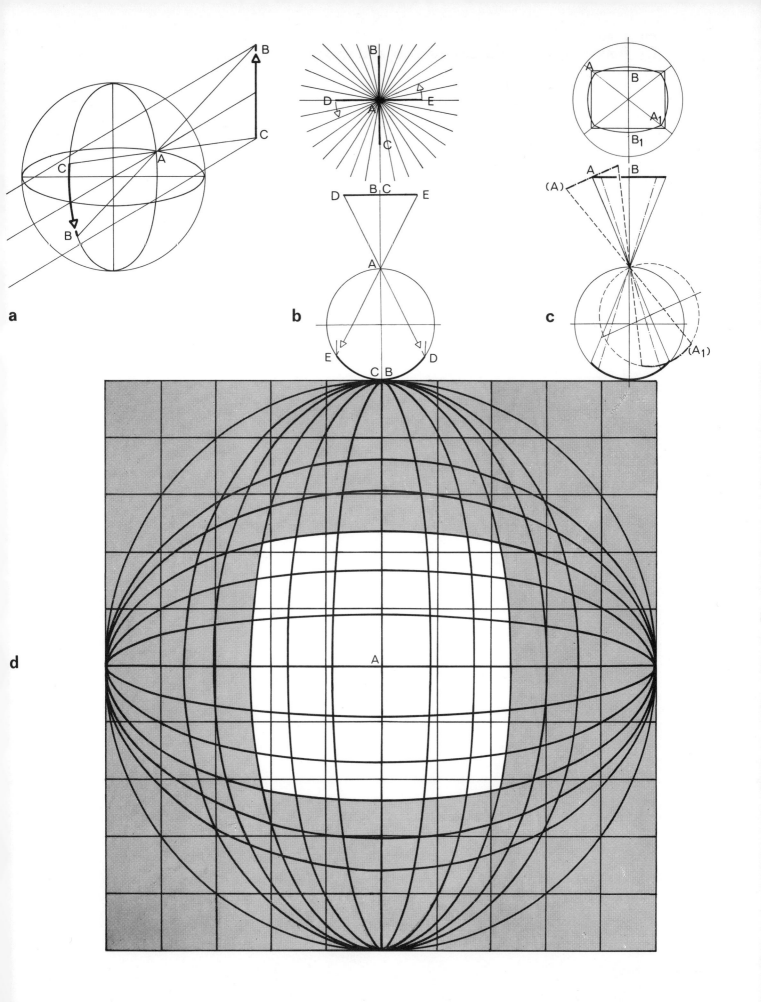

a

b

c

d

C. Rounded Forms: Helices, Arches, and Vaults

C Rounded Forms: Helices, Arches, and Vaults

In working out details, the geometrical form must be clearly defined before the final design and its execution in a specific material can be decided upon. In order to develop the architectural concept into a reality, the technical drawing, the statics, and the kind of material are developed simultaneously until the plan for the building project is finally completed.

The following examples give a summary of the geometircal forms that have practical implications to architects. They start with the simple rounded forms—the cylinder, the cone, and the sphere—which appear in building as details (pipes, arches, etc.) or as large forms (vaults, domes, silos, etc.). At the same time, their shadow constructions are visual examples of intersection problems and a design aid in the development of spatial relationships.

Because each turn brings about a difference in height, the helix, in its different forms, is the basis of many details.

Arches and vaults have had great significance in architectural history. New construction technology and building materials have affected these forms and increased their possible application. The further development of these forms technologically and architecturally can be one of the most fascinating aspects of a design.

In the following examples, only the basic geometrical forms of the bodies and the geometrical construction resulting from combining these are shown, rather than fine-detail solutions. This material is selected so that any problem that might occur in practice is at least discussed in principle, and, hopefully, solutions for most special cases can be found within these examples.

1 Chapel for the Air Force Academy, Colorado Springs, Colorado. Architects: Skidmore, Owings and Merrill, New York.

2 Stairway in an administrative building, Paris. Architects: D. Badani, A. Kandijan, P. Roux-Dorlut, and M. Folliason, Paris.

3 A tent for the National Garden Show, Cologne, 1957. Architect: Frei Otto, Stuttgart. Associate Architects: Siegfried Lohs, Ewald Bubner, and Diether R. Frank.

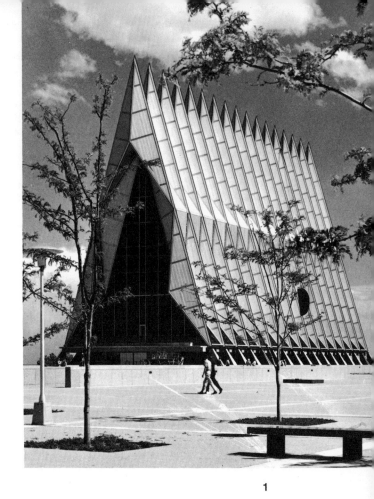

1

2

3

C1 Cylinders: Simple Intersection

a Two half-cylinders of different sizes, which intersect at 90° in plan. In elevation, the intersection curve is hidden by the small cylinder. The points of intersection are determined in plan with the aid of vertical cutting planes (thin lines). The auxiliary plane I goes through the crown; plane II is selected as desired. In the side view, the auxiliary planes are horizontal section lines (surface lines) on the small cylinder. The points of intersection lie where they meet on the large cylinder.

Transfer the vertical cutting planes from the side view to the plan at a and b distances apart. Construct the intersection curve on the surface of the cylinder through corresponding points of intersection of the mutually perpendicular cutting planes. For accuracy in the construction of larger curves, more cutting planes must be drawn.

b The same half-cylinder as in a, above, with angle of intersection changed in plan. The intersection curve must be constructed with points in both plan and elevation. To determine the points of intersection, horizontal auxiliary planes are used as in a, above. These produce straight section lines (surface lines) on both cylinders in plan and elevation. The corresponding points of intersection, from which the intersection curve can be drawn, lie where the surface lines of the large and small cylinders intersect.

c The intersection of two half-cylinders of the same size. The horizontal auxiliary planes have the same interval on both cylinders. The intersection curves of two cylinders of the same size are always ellipses. Here both ellipses appear in plan as straight lines. (See also C13 c and C14 e.) When the axes of the cylinders do not intersect, a space curve (not confined to one plane) is obtained as intersection line. Such a construction is demonstrated in f, below.

Circle-Sphere Method

With the aid of the circle-sphere method, the intersection curves of two cylinders of different sizes can be constructed in a single plane of projection. A prerequisite is that the axes of the cylinders intersect and that they both be parallel to the plane of projection.

d A circle with the radius of the large cylinder is drawn about the intersection of the axes of the cylinders. This circle intersects the sides of the small cylinder at four points. Through two of these points, project a line parallel to the sides of the large cylinder. The intersection of this projection line with the axis of the small cylinder produces the crown S of the respective intersection curve. Further points on the curve may be obtained by drawing larger circles. Each will cut the side lines of both cylinders at four points. From these points, draw perpendiculars to both cylinder axes (dotted lines). Their intersections are points on the intersection curve.

e Circle-sphere method with inclined cylinders. A circle with the radius of the larger cylinder produces dimension a from the point of intersection with the small cylinder, as illustrated. This dimension is transferred perpendicular to the side lines of the large cylinder and, when projected onto the axis of the small cylinder, produces the crown-point of the intersection curve. Further points are obtained by drawing larger circles. From their intersection points

with the side lines of the large and small cylinders, draw perpendiculars to the cylinder axes. Their points of intersection produce the flat part of the intersection curve. The round part is drawn by transferring, for each corresponding point on the opposite side of the axis, the respective width and depth dimensions (b and c, illustrated) from the flat curve.

Construction of the Intersection Curve from Surface Lines

f One cylinder inclined to the picture plane in plan intersects another inclined to the horizontal plane in elevation. In this case the intersection curve can be drawn without any of the foregoing constructions. The necessary points are determined by drawing an elevation perpendicular to the axis of the large cylinder. Here the intersection points of the surface lines of the small inclined cylinder within the larger horizontal cylinder are determined. Surface lines (broken lines) are established from point A to the intersection point A' (highest point of the curve) and from point B to the intersection point B' (deepest point of the curve). Both surface lines and intersection points are transferred between plan and elevation views until the intersection curve is completed.

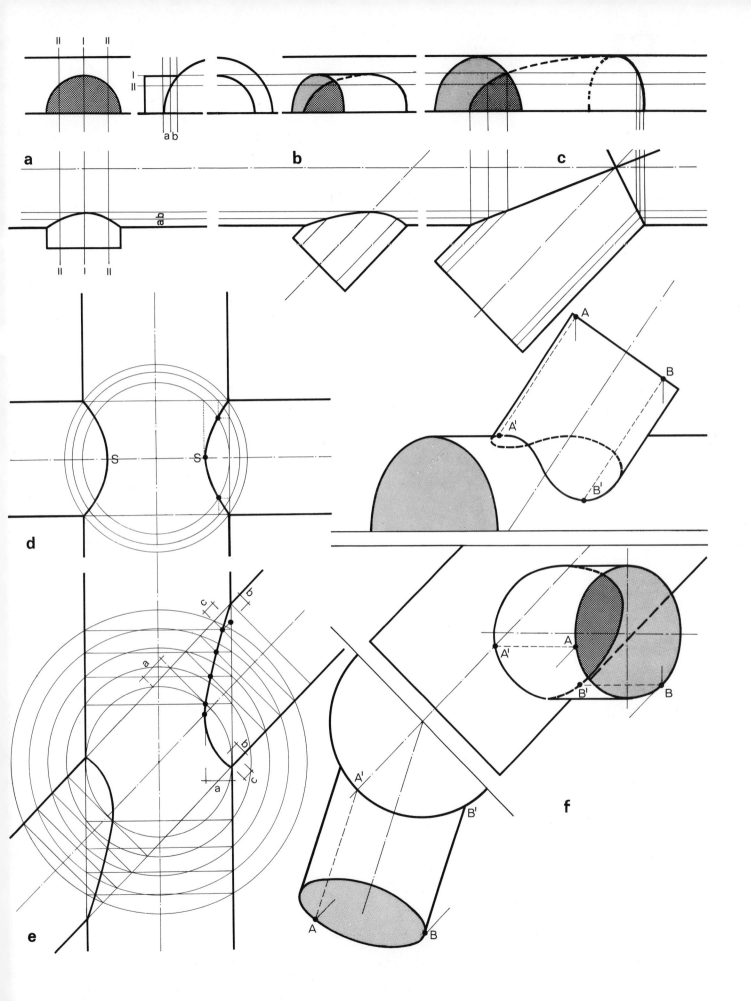

a

b

c

d

e

f

a A solid cylinder in plan and front and side elevations, with different inclined cutting planes (broken, heavy, and dot-dash lines). The section made by each cutting plane inclined to the cylinder axis produces an ellipse, which appears more compressed or elongated depending upon the angle of inclination. A cutting plane at 45° produces an ellipse, but it appears in front elevation as a circle.

Development of a Cylinder and the Truncated Cylinder

b The circumference of the cylinder is divided into equal parts (eight parts illustrated). Project the point of intersection of each element with each cutting plane onto the corresponding element of the stretchout or girth.

c Shade and shadow of a cylinder (repeat A13 **d**).

Shadow Projections on a Cylinder

d₁ Shadow of a square overhang. Determine the shade line on the cylinder with a tangent (light direction) at an angle of 45°, in plan. Construct, in plan, the shadows from the indicated points on the underside of the overhang. Transfer the shadow-producing points from the plan to the elevation. From each point in elevation, draw a 45° light ray, and on it project its shadowpoint from the plan. The three most important points are now drawn: the left corner, point 3, from which the shadow of the lower left edge runs as a straight line; the highest shadowpoint, 2', which stems from the bottom of the circle in plan; and the shadowpoint 1', which intersects the shade line of the cylinder. The lower front edge of the overhang produces an ellipse as its shadow, which, however, appears as a circle in elevation. The lower left edge also produces an ellipse as its shadow, which, however, appears as a straight line in elevation.

d₂ Shadow of an overhanging square similar to **d₁**, but rotated 45° in plan. The construction is as in **d₁**, above. The right side surface of the overhang is in half light.

d₃ Shadow of a round overhanging capital (low cylinder). The shade for the overhang is drawn as the shade on a cylinder. The shadow of the overhang is constructed as in **d₁**, above.

Shade and Shadows in a Hollow Cylinder

e Elevation of a circular opening, the side view (vertical section), and the plan (horizontal section). In the elevation, light rays are drawn as tangents at an angle of 45°. They provide starting points for the shade, 1 and 5. Draw light rays at an angle of 45° from other shadow-producing points to their points of intersection on the circle in elevation. Each intersection is a shadowpoint in elevation. In the side view, draw light rays inside the cylinder at an angle of 45° from the same points. Project the corresponding shadowpoint from the elevation onto each light ray. An ellipse results as the shadow curve. The points projected to the plan from the elevation and side view produce an ellipse of equal size.

f Shadow in a vaulted archway which, in plan, is inclined to the picture plane. The semicircle of the arch appears in the front elevation as an ellipse. The right, inside surface is visible. The light ray in elevation is projected at an angle of 45° and the light direction in plan is at an angle of 45° to the surface of the arch front. The shadows are constructed beginning with point 1. The arch is rotated parallel to the picture plane in order to have its opening in true size. The light ray, at an angle of 45° from point 1 (thin lines), produces, on the right side, the height of the shadow, point 1'. The light direction at an angle of 45° from point 1 in plan produces the depth of the shadow at 1s. The horizontal between 1s and 1' cuts the edge of the arch at point 1". Now, through any given point, the depth of its shadow can be determined by a line parallel to 1-1s, while its height can be determined by a line parallel to 1-1". The point at which the shadow starts can be obtained by rotating the arch parallel to the picture plane, then drawing a 45° tangent to the arch. It can also be determined by drawing a line parallel to 1-1" and tangent to the arch.

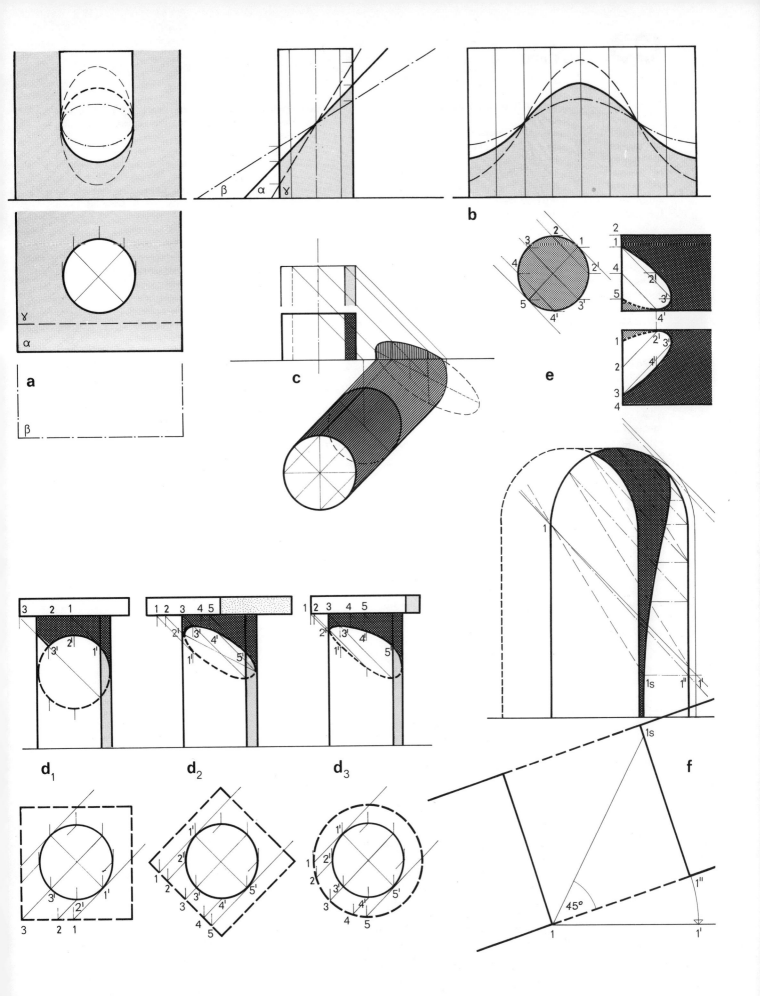

C3 The Cone

Conic Sections with Variously Inclined Planes

a A plane whose angle to the horizontal is less than that of the profile of the cone cuts the cone in an ellipse. The individual points of the section can easily be determined by the surface lines in plan and elevation. The incline of the cutting plane causes the section ellipse to appear shortened in plan. In order to determine its true size, rotate the ellipse into the horizontal plane.

b A plane whose angle to the axis or the horizontal is the same as that of the profile of the cone cuts the cone in a parabola. Pertinent section points are easily determined through auxiliary horizontal planes I and II. In elevation, these planes appear as horizontal lines, and on the surface of the cone they cut the section at points on the parabola. The auxiliary planes I and II produce section circles in plan, onto which the points are transferred from the elevation. The incline of the cutting plane causes the parabola to appear shortened in plan. In order to determine its true size, revolve the parabola into the horizontal plane.

c A plane whose angle of inclination to the axis is smaller than that of the elements cuts the cone in a hyperbolic section. Construction is as in **b,** above. In order to determine its true size, revolve the hyperbola into the horizontal plane.

Shade and Shadow of a Cone

The size of the shade and shadow of a cone is dependent upon the angle of its elements. If the angle is less than the true angle of the light ray, then the cone is entirely in light.

d The shade and shadows of a cone can only be constructed from the shadow cast by the apex of the cone (see illustration).

e Cone in plan and elevation. The shadow of the apex is drawn at an angle of 45°. The tangents from the apex of the cone's shadow in plan form the shadow limits on the ground plane and establish the beginning points for the shade on the cone. The shade appears on the surface of the cone from tangent point T to apex S. The corresponding tangent in plan is the shadow of line TS.

f Reclining hollow cone in elevation (above) and horizontal section. The shadow of the apex is drawn at an angle of 45° in the direction opposite the light source. Point A in the axis of the direction of light produces the shadowpoint A', which falls most deeply in the interior of the hollow cone. It falls on the interior surface of the cone and, in the elevation, lies at an angle of 45° from the midpoint of the cone (in the axis of the direction of light). Further points of the shadow curve are determined by auxiliary planes (I and II). These planes appear in section as straight lines; in the elevation, as circles. The shadow figure inside the hollow cone is produced by the circle in the elevation. The shadowpoints on the auxiliary planes are obtained by determining, at a 45° angle, the position of the midpoints M_1 and M_2 on the respective auxiliary planes I and II. From each point, project a line to the 45° light ray in the elevation. From each point of inter-

section, draw a circle whose diameter is the same as the base of the cone. These circles intersect respective cutting plane circles in shadowpoints.

g Circular opening composed of a hollow cone and a hollow cylinder, in section and elevation. Shadow construction is as in **f,** above, with three auxiliary planes I, II, and III by which shadowpoints are determined.

Intersection of a Steep and a Flat Cone

h The intersection points of the surfaces of both cones appear in elevation as a straight line and in plan as a circle. The shade and shadows on this body are a combination of the shade of the flat cone, the shade of the steep cone, and a part of the shadow which the steep cone throws on the flat cone. The shade and the shadows in plan are constructed for both cones as in **e,** above. The shadow on the flat cone is created by a shadow plane, which is steeper than its surface lines and therefore forms a hyperbola (see **c,** above). The crown of the hyperbola lies where the shade of the steep cone begins. Its base points B_1 and B_2 lie where the shadow limit lines of the steep cone intercept the base of the flat cone in plan. Further points on the hyperbola may be constructed by horizontal auxiliary planes where, as in the plan, the points are found. The auxiliary plane I produces points C_1 and C_2 in this manner. The auxiliary plane II produces points D_1 and D_2. For a better illustration of the shadow form created, a side view, perpendicular to the direction of light, is drawn.

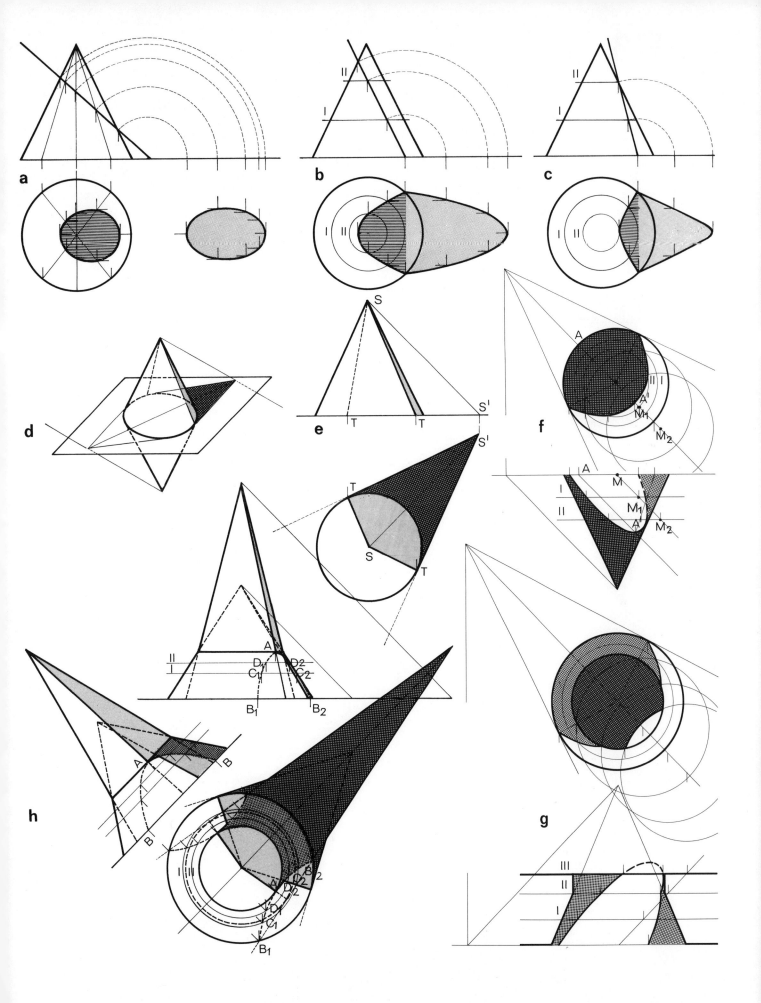

C4 The Sphere

Spheric Sections

The sphere is the only body whose elevation appears from every direction; that is, as a circle. Each selected plane which cuts the sphere produces a circle in section.

Shade and Shadows of a Sphere

a The sphere intercepted by light rays produces a shade cylinder. Its shadow appears as a section of this cylinder.

b Shade and shadows of a sphere in plan and elevation. The light rays as tangents to the sphere at 45° produce in elevation the points 1 and 2; in plan, the points 3 and 4. In both projections the shade appears as an ellipse whose major axis lies between these points of tangency. Draw an elevation perpendicular to the 45° angle (here, above and left of plan); the light rays appear in this elevation at their true angle of inclination (see A12 **b**). Drawn as tangents to the sphere, they produce the highest point, 5, and the lowest point, 6, of the shade. The shade line appears in this elevation as a straight line; the upper half of the sphere is in light, the lower half is in its own shade. In plan, the points 5 and 6 provide the minor axis of the shade-ellipse and the major axis of the shadow-ellipse.

c Sphere shade and shadows constructed from the elevation only. The simplest method of constructing the shade of the sphere is by drawing the light rays as tangents to the sphere. Thus points 1 and 2 are established. The horizontal distance from point 1 to point 2 projected onto the horizontal axis produces points 3 and 4, and projected onto the vertical axis produces points 5 and 6. The elliptical line of the shade on the sphere can be constructed according to the ellipse construction A14 **f.** The highest point of the shade-ellipse is found by laying a tangent to the sphere at the true angle of the light ray (point 7). Its actual position on the surface of the sphere is obtained when its distance from the vertical axis is rotated 45° (dotted line). Directly opposite this point, through the mid-point and at the same distance from it, lies the deepest point, point 8.

The Hollow Sphere

In construction, the hollow sphere is used principally as a partial form. In a spherical enclosure, for example, its outer spherical form is more important for the construction and the drawing than the space within the hollow sphere. For the construction, it is important to note that each intersection of a plane with the hollow sphere produces a circular section.

Shade and Shadows in a Hollow Hemisphere

d A hollow hemisphere in plan and, above it, the view into the opening of the hemisphere. In the elevation, draw the 45° light rays as tangents to the circle in view. The points of tangency are the beginning points for the shadow. Further shadowpoints are found with the aid of a side view perpendicular to the angle of the light ray (above, right). In this view, the light ray appears in its true angle of inclination (A12 **b**). In the elevation, auxiliary planes are laid through points 1 to 5 of the visible circle, in the direction of the light rays. In the side view, the intersections appear as circles on which the desired shadowpoints lie. From the side view, transfer the shadowpoints to the main elevation, then from there to the plan. The shadow in the side view is a straight line; in both front view and plan it is a half ellipse.

e The elevation is of a niche, consisting of a hollow half-cylinder with a hollow quarter-sphere above it, and a horizontal hollow hemisphere below it (imagine a round basin for a fountain). In the construction of the shadows, start at point 1 on the left side edge of the hollow cylinder. Its shadow falls partly in the hollow cylinder and partly in the horizontal hollow hemisphere. It appears in plan as a straight line. In the front elevation, the shadow appears in the hollow cylinder as a straight line and in the hollow hemisphere below it as a half-ellipse. The shadow in the hollow quarter-sphere is constructed with a side view corresponding to **d,** above. In this side view, the last shadowpoint falling within the hollow sphere is determined. It lies at point 2′, where the shadow line intersects the border circle between the hollow half-cylinder and the hollow quarter-sphere. This imaginary border circle appears in the auxiliary side view as an ellipse (dotted line). From the shadowpoint 2′, determine the shadow-producing point 2 on the circle in view, using the light direction. The shadowpoints between 1′ and 2′ fall, of course, in the hollow cylinder, and they can now be easily constructed in plan and elevation. The shadow in the horizontal hollow hemisphere corresponds to the construction in **d,** above, rotated 90°.

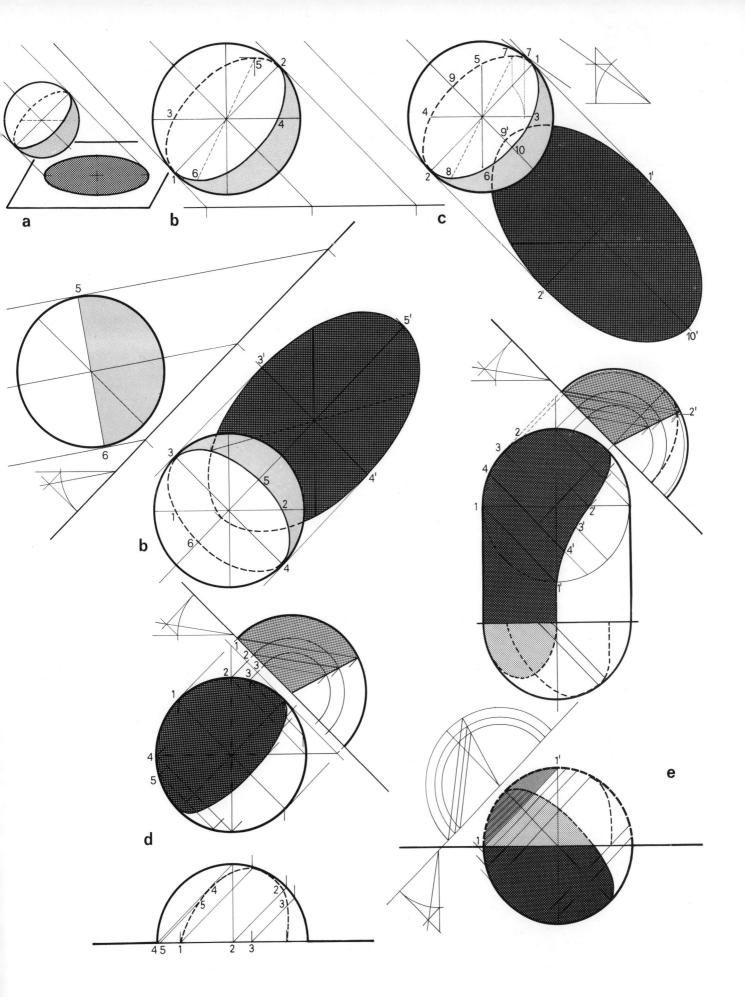

a

b

c

b

d

e

C5 Light and Shade Zones

Out of doors, light and shade seldom appear in the clear separations and outlines shown in the examples here. Geometrically, sun rays are not completely parallel. The light is diffused by the air. Therefore, the transition from light to shade on rounded surfaces is never so clear as in the drawing. Light and shade appear in different intensities, each according to how the body stands in relation to the direction of the light or according to the angle from which the body is viewed in relation to other bodies. The drawings opposite attempt to explain how light divides or distributes itself on a particular body.

Light Intensity on a Plane

a A plane positioned perpendicular to the direction of light is struck by a certain number of light rays. If the plane is rotated out of this direction, it becomes pierced with correspondingly fewer light rays. When the plane is positioned exactly in the direction of the light, it does not directly intercept any light rays; it receives indirect or side light. The light intensity on a plane is greatest when the plane is perpendicular to the light direction, and least when the plane is parallel to the light direction.

Direct and Reflected Light on a Sphere

b The difference between the light intensity of direct and reflected light on surfaces with different positions in relation to the light source is best shown on the sphere, since its surface has all possible angles of inclination to the direction of light. The zone of the greatest intensity lies toward the light source in the axis of the light direction. On the circle, where the light rays are tangent to the sphere (shade line, see C4 **a–c**), the light intensity is least. The part of the sphere which lies in its own shade also appears to be in different light zones (or shade zones) due to the reflected light of the environs. The brilliant pole of the sphere facing the light corresponds to an opposite pole which is lighter than the rest of the surface in shade, due to reflected light on that half. For better illustration, and in order to graphically indicate the light intensity, divide the sphere surface into zones for which a uniform light intensity in each zone is assumed.

Construction of the Light and Shade Zones

c On a sphere, divide both the side in light and the side in shade into five zones each with the same light and shade intensity in each zone. The construction of the shade line and the zone limits (zone circles should be perpendicular to the light direction) is carried out as in C4 **b,** above.

Light and Shade Zones on a Round Body

d Light and shade zones for any object can be constructed using the sphere as a basis. A round body, closely related to the sphere, is illustrated. The construction points for the limits of each zone are transferred from the sphere to the body for the respective angle of inclination of light. In the example, intervals are drawn for three angles. The same angles of inclination create a cone on the surface of the sphere. The zone limits must be enlarged proportionally. Here the intervals between zone limits are transferred from line AA on the sphere to line BB on the torus by means of an auxiliary cone whose elements are tangent to the sphere.

Light and Shade Zones on a Vase

e Draw the same light and shade zones on the spherical part of the vase corresponding to **c,** above. The zone limits on the cone-shaped upper and lower parts are developed from the intersection of the cone and the sphere, and from corresponding zone-limit lines of opposite cones. The zone limits on the cylindrical part are developed from the zone-limit lines of a sphere whose diameter is the same as that of the cylinder. A horizontal section through the center of the sphere intersects the zone-limit lines in points with the same relative location as the limit lines of the cylinder.

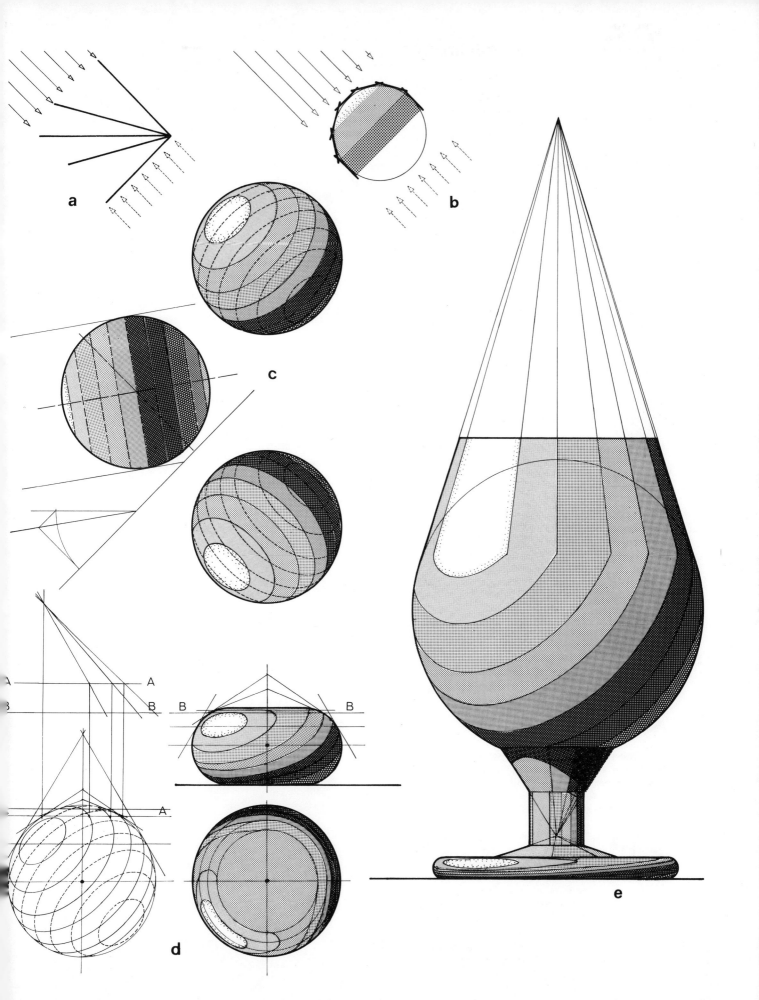

a

b

c

d

e

C6 Shade and Shadows of Round Bodies

As a rule, with complicated bodies, construct the shade and then the shadow. In example **a,** the shadow (above) overlaps the shade.

A Cavetto Form Between Two Cylinders

a For the construction of the shade, draw the light rays in the elevation as 45° tangents to the cavetto (curved molding): points 1 and 2. Because the shade is symmetrical to the light direction, another shadowpoint, 3, lies in the elevation in the center axis on the same height as point 1. The shade line on the cylinder is determined from the plan, as in C2 **c.** Accordingly, points 4 and 5 are established. The uppermost point of the shadow curve, 6, is found by drawing in the true angle of the light ray (broken line) tangent to the cavetto, point 6′ (see plan), whose distance from the center axis is revolved into the axis at an angle of 45° in plan. In order to determine another shadowpoint, 7, draw an auxiliary horizontal plane I-I through the body. From its points of intersection with the curved molding, draw the cone in the elevation and in plan with the aid of tangents. Construct the shade for this point according to C3 **e.** The shade point found at the base of the cone is the desired point 7.

b The beginning point of the shadow, 8, can only be found by following the auxiliary construction illustrated in **b.** Draw an auxiliary cutting plane II-II vertically through the center of the body, in plan. On this plane, the shadow of the upper shadow-casting circle appears as an ellipse (see C2 **c**). Point 8 lies in the elevation where the ellipse intersects the cavetto. On the center axis, at the same height, lies point 9. The uppermost point of the shadow curve, 10, is found by drawing the true angle of the light ray from the lower edge of the deck onto the cavetto and by rotating the horizontal dimension thus established 45° in plan (compare point 6).

c In order to determine another shadowpoint, 11, draw a horizontal auxiliary plane III-III through the body. On it the shadow appears as a circle and the shadowpoint, 11, lies where the circular shadow line intersects the section of the body on the same plane. The lowest point of the shadow, 12, is found in the same way as point 8.

Shadow in a Circular Opening

d The shade and shadow construction of a cavetto are shown in **a.** The circular opening in **d** corresponds to the hollow form of the upper part of **a.**
The shade and shadows in this opening are constructed with the aid of spheres, which are drawn around it. The shade points of the spheres in the axis between the midpoints of the spheres and the opening are shade points inside the cavetto form. These points produce shadows on the opposite side. In order to determine the shadowpoints, draw a section in the light direction. In this section the light ray appears in its true angle of inclination. The shadowpoints are determined individually in this section view. Point 1 (from the principal axis of the light direction) and point 2 (from the elevation) are illustrated. Left, the view into the opening, drawn from the light direction. The lower inside edge is both shade and shadow line.

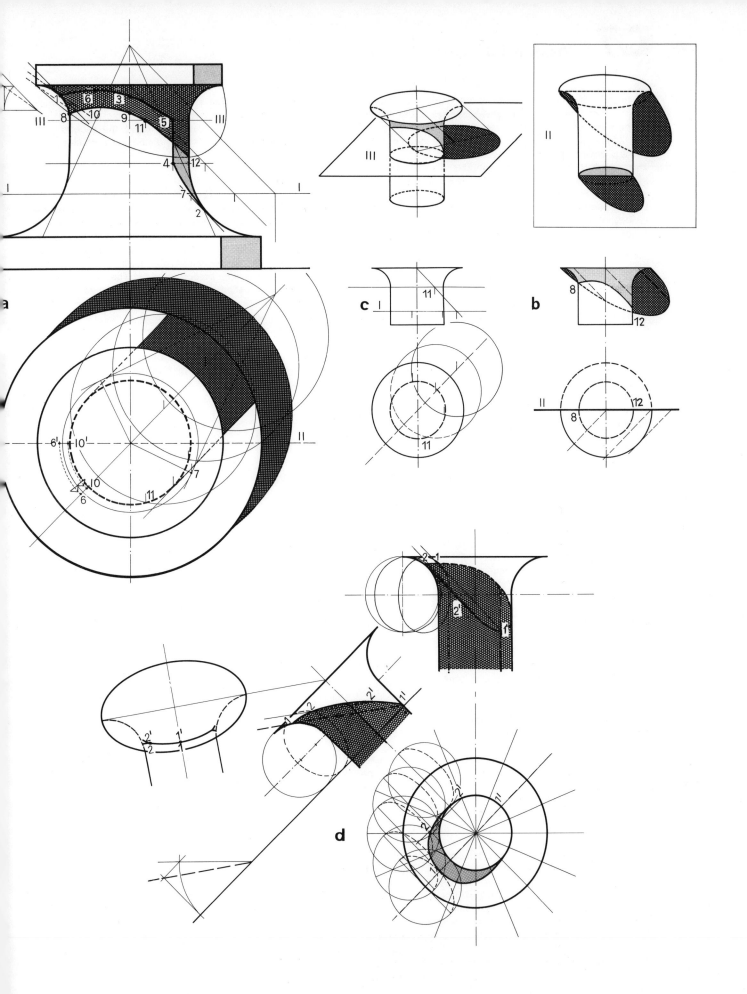

a Imagine the earth's sphere to be transparent and its axis to be a pole. Thus, figuratively speaking, the shadow of the pole moves around the equator once in 24 hours. The 24 hours corresponds to 360°, 1 hour equals 15°, 4 minutes equals 1°, 1 minute equals 15′.

This model is the basis of all sundials. The shadow pole (gnomon) always points skyward to the north and stands parallel to the axis of the earth. Its inclination to the horizon is the same as the geographic latitude of the locality. One speaks of equatorial, horizontal, or vertical sundials, according to the inclination of the faceplate—that is, the hour circle.

Equatorial Sundial

b The face of the equatorial sundial lies parallel to the earth's equator, and is pierced vertically by the shadow stake. The hour angle always amounts to 15°. The face of this dial is usually executed as a curved band. If an equatorial tilted plane is used instead, its underside must be divided also.

Portable sundials must be constructed so that they may be set for different geographic latitudes, if they are to work accurately at any location. For this purpose, the equatorial sundial is best.

Horizontal and Vertical Sundials

Faceplates for horizontal and vertical sundials are constructed as follows. The circular face of the equatorial sundial is surrounded with a circular cylinder. The hour divisions are drawn thereon as surface elements. The points of intersection of these elements in a horizontal or vertical plane produce the desired sundial face.

c As an example, a horizontal and a vertical sundial are constructed for Stuttgart, Germany, 49° north latitude, 9° east longitude. The vertical area (house wall) does not face exactly south, but is turned 30° to the west.

Difference Between Local Time and Zone Time

All sundials show local time; that is, they show 12 o'clock when the sun is due south. Central European time is a zone time which is only exact for places with 15° east longitude (Görlitz). In Stuttgart (9° east longitude) the sun is not due south at 12 o'clock, but 6 × 4 = 24 minutes later. In order for the sundial to show local zone time, the hour divisions must be corrected by rotating the numbers of the equatorial dial (faceplate) 6° to the right.

In order to construct the 8 o'clock point, for example, draw its position on the 24-hour circular face. (Assume this to be the cross-section of a cylinder. Rotate it 90° clockwise along the axis of the shadow stake, thus revealing a side view of the imaginary cylinder.) Extend the 8 o'clock point along the surface line (broken line) until it pierces the wall in elevation. In plan (the horizontal sundial), the 8 o'clock point lies vertically below the base-piercing point of the above-mentioned surface line, at the distance b from the major axis. Project a line parallel to the major axis until it pierces the plan view of the wall. The 8 o'clock point lies vertically above in the elevation. In order to obtain the face of the sundial in true size,

construct another plan view, perpendicular to the house wall. How the face of the sundial and the shadow stake appear on the wall is illustrated above the second plan. For the 2 o'clock point (14), the dimension a applies.

Time Differential

d Because of the elliptical orbit of the earth around the sun, the time differs between the two meridional orbits. These seconds add up, in the course of a year, to approximately 15 minutes. From the graphic illustration, this time differential can be determined; that is, how many minutes the sundial time must be corrected by. The resulting curve (thick line) is based on the factors developed from the varying projections of the orbit on the equator (broken line) and from the changing orbital speed of the earth around the sun (dotted line). [**Note:** It is a simple matter to determine the correct placement of a sundial "set" for one of the five time zones in the United States, after which, of course, the same kind of calculations would follow.]

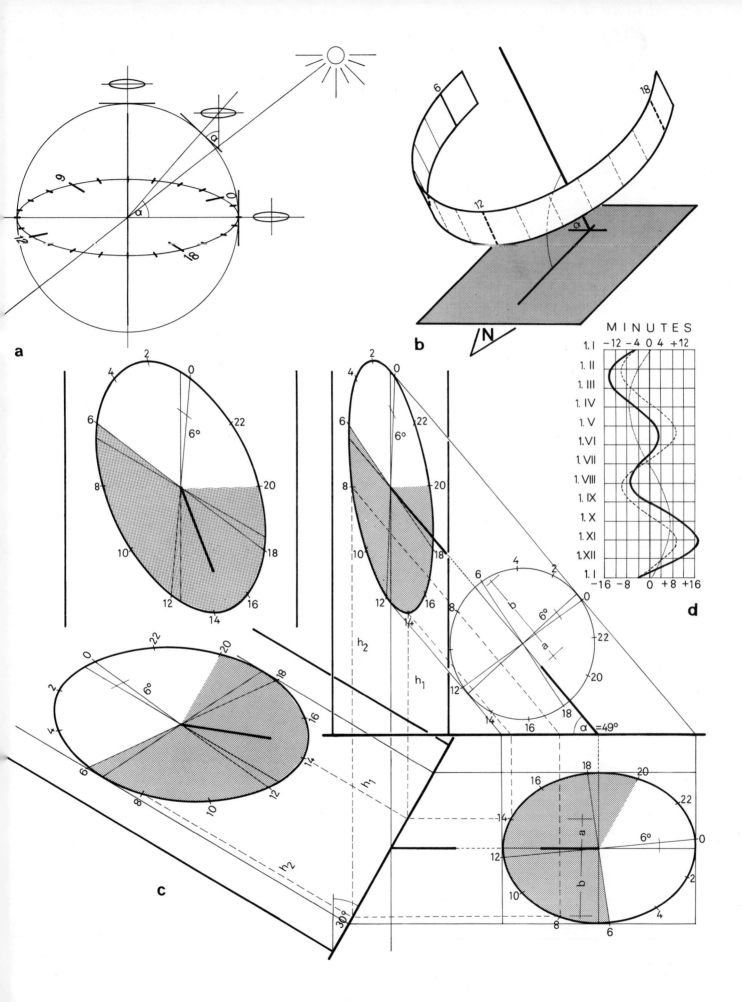

93

C8 The Helix, the Helicoid, Screw (Spiral) Forms

[Note: The remaining sections of the book (except for the last one on pp. 110–111) are of limited usefulness to the architectural draftsman except as exercises to sharpen his understanding of perspective.]

A point which moves in a circle and, at the same time, climbs uniformly produces a helix. It is steeper or flatter according to the circumference of the circle (in plan) and the height it travels in one revolution (in elevation).

The Helix

a The circle in plan is divided into 16 equal parts, which correspond to 16 divisions of the height or lead-per-revolution. Beginning with point 0, transfer each division point from plan directly above to the elevation at the corresponding height. The helix is obtained by the connection of each point in elevation. For a more exacting curve, increase the number of divisions in both plan and elevation, or draw tangents through the individual points that determine the helix. The latter method will assist in the completion of the drawing with a French curve.

The Development of the Helix

b In its development, the helix is an ascending straight line. It is determined from the length of the parts in the circle in plan and from the height of the individual points, plotted in elevation directly above.

Tangents to the Helix

In the development, the helix and its tangents lie in a common straight line. In plan, **a,** the tangents to the helix are tangents to the circle whose individual lengths can be transferred from the development. Connection of the end points of the tangents in plan forms a spiral curve. The angle of the tangents in the elevation is obtained from the connection of corresponding points on the spiral curve in plan, and the point of tangency to the circle.

The Helicoid

c When the radius of a circle rotates itself about a uniformly ascending midpoint, it describes a helicoid. In practice, the entire radius is never used to produce the helicoidal surface. In the example, it is developed from line AB of the radius MB.

Development of the Helicoid

b The helicoid has different inclines. It increases as it approaches the axis about which it revolves. The development using the radius MB corresponds to the development of the helix in **a,** above. In addition, helix developments using smaller radii MA (broken line) and MC (dot dash line) are drawn in.

The Screw

d A screw exists when, by circular rotation about its axis, a certain profile advances uniformly (in the direction of its axis). According to use and purpose, there are screws with different profiles and windings (e.g., wood screws and metal screws). Illustrated is a screw with a sharp V profile.

Screw Forms

e Screw form created by a square.

f Screw form created by a rectangle.
The forms **e** and **f** are created when the individual points of the figure in plan execute circular rotation and uniform rise. Similar forms or surfaces can be produced by rotation of a square or rectangular rod (e.g., when a wrought-iron rod is heated and twisted).

Spiral Pipe

g For the construction, imagine the pipe as a row of spheres with the same diameter as the pipe, whose midpoints lie on the spiral curve. For the elevation of the spiral pipe, draw a continuous curve tangent to the individual spheres.

a

b

16 15 14 13 12 11 10 9 8 7 6 5 4 3 2 1

0   1   2   3   4   5   6   7   8

c

M   A   Ç   B

8   9
7   10
6   11
5   12
4   13
3   2   14
1   0   15

d   e   f   g

C9 Spiral Stairs

The simplest form of spiral stairs consists of a round wooden column with steps let into it. There are spiral stairways with one full column, some of which are tubular; others have a partial column built onto each individual step.

A Simple Spiral Stairway of Stone

a The steps are designed so that each contains its own column for one rise. By placing one step on top of the other, the entire column is developed in a cylindrical form. The circle in plan is divided here into 16 equal parts, which correspond to 16 risers.

Right winding. The stairs spiral to the right, a basic recommendation for all spiral stairs, since most people are right-handed and hold the railing with their right hands. Also, on right-winding stairs the narrow tread of the inside steps causes the stairway to be more easily ascended than descended.

b The development of the stair steps shows the tread width to be greatest on the outside, while in the center (in the line of travel), the tread width is normal. On spiral stairs, an accepted rise-to-run proportion of steps (twice the rise plus the run equals 24 to 25) refers to dimensions in the line of travel. The smallest run is at the column, but in any case it should be no less than four inches.

The Bottom View of Massive Steps

The most attractive design of the underside of a spiral stair is the helicoidal surface. This is achieved by individual steps which correspond to the toned area in the development **b,** above. The sharp angle on the outside of the step is difficult to make and fragile in laying. Detailing of the joint at a right angle to the development line creates a helicoidal surface (see b_1, step profile with 90° joints), which, because of the joint, is not easy to produce.

The Column

c_1 The simplest form, where front and back edges of the step are executed as tangents to the circular partial column. This form results in a very sharp angle at the column, created by the steps as they are placed one on top of another.

c_2 The front edge of the step is laid out in line with the midpoint of the column. This entails a great deal of work if the steps are of stone (especially hard stone).

c_3 The front edge of the step is laid out tangent to a circle whose diameter is larger than that of the column. From the point of tangency, continue the edge perpendicular to the midpoint of the column. This solution is geometrically simple and leads to good results.

Basic Considerations for the Construction

d Just as straight-run stairs span between either two walls or two fixed supports (carriages) (d_1), the spiral stairs can also be spanned between two supports; one wall and column (d_2) or carriages (d_3). Also, as a cantilevered, straight-run stairway (d_4), spiral stairways may be cantilevered from a wall (d_5) or from its own column (d_6). Illustrated in d_7 is a spiral stairway with hanging steps, in d_8, a spiral stairway supported on a beam.

From these basic considerations, together with material selection and a review of geometrical relationships according to **a** and **b,** above, details for each spiral stairway are worked out. The clearer the basic form, the more neatly the detail can be solved. Special consideration must be given to the connections and points of change in direction (e.g., the continuation of a handrail which follows the incline of the stairs and then continues horizontally or on another incline).

Construction of Circular Carriages

e Carriages of wood or steel are bent over a cylinder which has the same diameter as the stairs in plan.

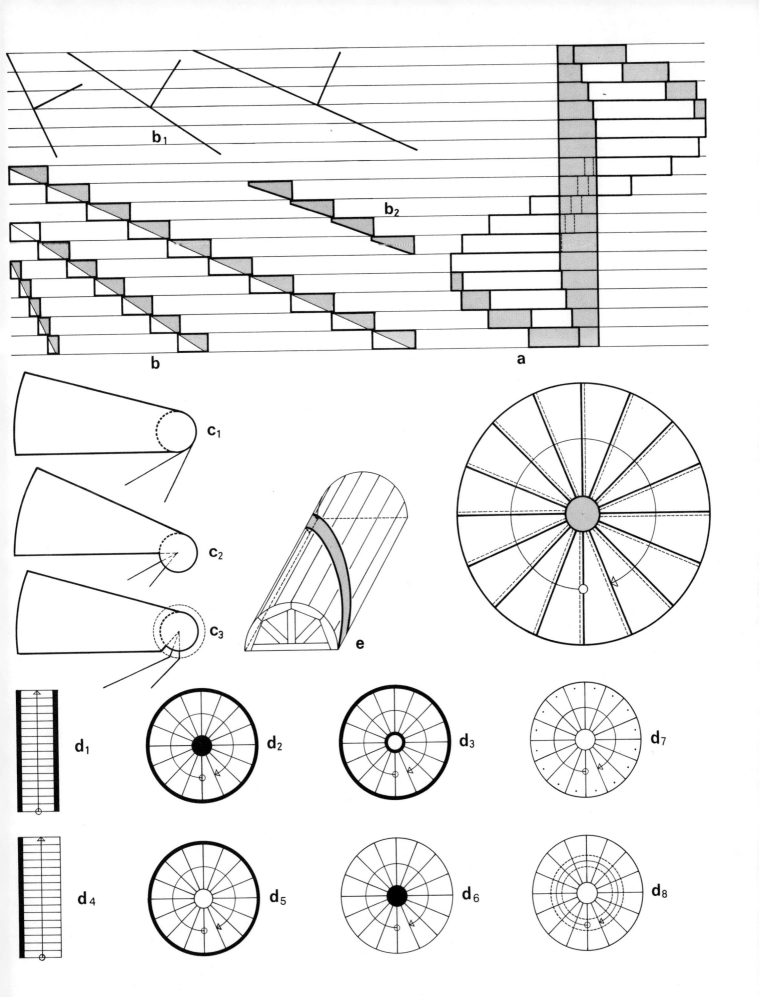

C10 Winding Stairways

In terms of geometry and construction, the simplest way to accomplish the transition from one height to another is the straight-run stairway. Usually, it is also the best architectural solution. However, a turn in the run of the stairway may be necessary for various reasons, such as shortening the run, different locations of landings, and architectural design. The possibilities range from the quarter-turn (90°) to the full spiral stairway.

a₁ The straight-run stairway. This requires the greatest length (the length of the stairway plus the landings). Landings should always be somewhat longer than the width of the stairs; otherwise it will seem narrow visually.

a₂ The 90° winder. By using the 90° winder, the required length in the principal direction can be shortened.

a₃ The 180° winder in the direction of the principal run. In using the 180° winder, the required length in the principal direction can be shortened by two landings.

a₄ The 180°-turn stairway consists of two straight-run stairways, each of which spans one-half of one story, and an intermediate landing, at one-half of the vertical distance between the two consecutive floors. It is, in construction and architecturally, preferable to the winding stairway, if enough space is available.

a₅ The 180° winder with two short, straight flights reduces its length by at least a part of the intermediate landing of the 180°-turn stairway.

a₆ The 270° winder requires even less space than the 180° winder in **a₅**, above. However, it needs special consideration in its construction and detailing.

a₇ The spiral stairway needs the least amount of space in plan. Its geometric construction is described in C9.

Laying Out the Steps

b, c When two straight runs and a half-spiral are schematically put together to form a 180° winder, the transition from one slope to another, where the straight run and the spiral join, together with the narrow treads on the inside, make the stairs difficult to climb. This is shown clearly by **c,** where the development of the interior and the exterior sides are compared with the center line of travel (thick line).

d Assume the tread width on the inside of the stairway to be the same throughout. In this situation the front edges of the steps run at so sharp an angle to the normal line of travel that the stairs are difficult to climb.
The best design is achieved when only a few of the steps must be distorted. The transition from the winding steps to the normal steps is best achieved by one of the following methods, which are mentioned here only for the geometrical procedure. For the solution of details, a study of good books on staircase construction is recommended.

Laying Out by Proportional Division

e The points of intersection of the extended front edge

of the steps with the staircase axis shifted proportionally. Along the center axis of the stairway, the distance from the midpoint of the turn to the front edge of the last pair of winding steps is divided into as many parts as there are pairs of winding steps to be laid out. In the example, the front edge of one step lies in the axis of the stairway; 7 winding steps and 3 pairs of straight-run steps are laid out. Along the axis of the stairway, the proportions $1:2:3:4:5:6$ are marked off. The front edges of the steps are determined by connecting the points along the uniformly divided center line of travel with the division points along the axis of the stairway. In order to improve the transition from the winding steps to the normal steps, shift the front edge of the last pair of involved steps forward an additional inch.

Laying Out by the Division Circle

f In the example, the middle of a step lies in the center axis of the staircase. From the front edge of the last normal step (in this case, 1 and 14), construct a semicircle about the crown of the winding and divide it into as many parts as there are steps to lay out. The connecting lines from the division points perpendicular to the axis of the stairs establish the beginning point for the front edge of the winding steps. The front edge of the last pair of steps in the winding is shifted forward an additional inch as in **e,** above.

Laying Out in the Development

g Plan of a 90° winder. Steps 5 through 10 are laid out to the center of convergence (broken lines). The development on the right shows the steep, narrow steps in the winding which are difficult to climb. To improve this, steps 4 through 11 should be re-aligned. Draw the development of the inside of the steps and connect steps 3 and 12 with a straight line. Divide the line into four equal parts and from the first and third points construct alternating perpendiculars. From steps 3 and 12, construct alternating perpendiculars to the respective stair incline. The intersection of the two sets of perpendiculars establishes the midpoints for two arcs which determine the heights of steps 4 to 11. Thus, the profile of the stairs is determined in the development and can be transferred to the plan (heavy lines). Also, in this case, both of the last two normal steps are re-aligned, as in **e,** above.

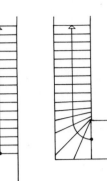
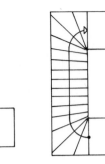
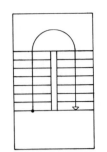
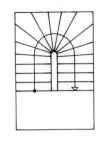
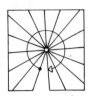
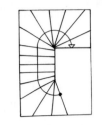

a₁　　**a₂**　　　**a₃**　　　　**a₄**　　　　　**a₅**　　　　　**a₆**　　　　**a₇**

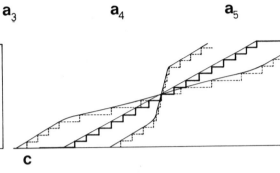
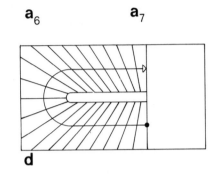

b　　　　　**c**　　　　　　　　　　**d**

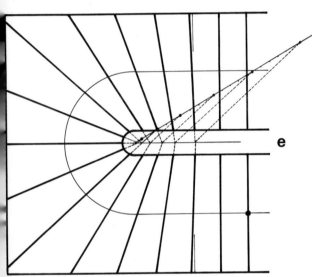
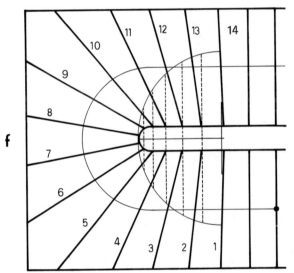

e　　　　　　　　　　　　　**f**

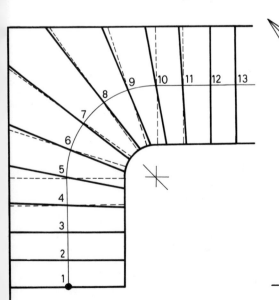
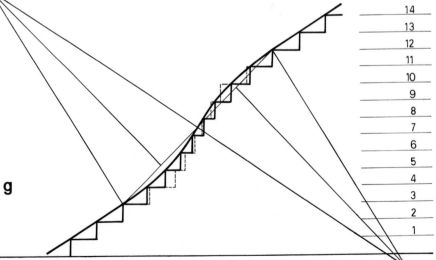

g

C11 The 180°-Turn Stairway

The Basic Form

a The 180°-turn stairway can be constructed as a straight-run stairway with a short flight from the floor concerned to an intermediate landing. Critical points, which demand a perfect geometrical solution, originate primarily in the area encircled and marked A, which is the point where the stairway changes direction. In plan, strive for a clear relationship between the steps of both flights. Also, try to make the bottom surface of both connecting flights meet at a common point on the intermediate landing (e.g., point K in illustration **b**).

Thickness of Landing and Carriage

b When the vertically measured thickness, h, of the carriage or slab supporting the steps is the same as that of the landing, the break between the bottom surfaces of both flights and their common landing (point K) runs in a straight line. The first step down from the intermediate landing lies one tread ahead of the first step going up from the same landing.

Risers of Both Flights in Line and the Break at the Landing in a Straight Line

c This requirement can only be filled when the thickness, H, of the landing is greater than the thickness, h, of the slab supporting the stairs. The proportions between the rise a, the tread b, and the distance i of the front edge of the step from the break line K at the bottom of the landing can be calculated using the following formula:

1st step up:
$$e = H - h$$
$$i : e = b : a$$
$$i = \frac{e \cdot b}{a}$$

1st step down:
$$c = \sqrt{a^2 + b^2}$$
$$\frac{h}{d} = \frac{c}{b}$$
$$h = \frac{d \cdot c}{b}$$
$$g = a + h - H$$
$$i : g = b : a$$
$$i = \frac{g \cdot b}{a}$$

A Curved Change in Direction

The transition from one direction to another is sometimes executed in a curve. The geometrically perfect detailing of this curve is important for the carriage (or similar support) as well as for the handrail. The simplest form is achieved when the turn continues horizontally. For this solution, however, more space is necessary, because the curve adds to the length of the stairs. If this space is not available, the curve must be executed on an incline. A helicoidal surface is thus created on its top and bottom sides.

Schematic Illustration of a Curved Change in Direction

d Plan and elevation of the top of the curved surface. The heights are obtained from the incline of the stairway and the radii of the curved surface. When the radius of the ramp r = 1, its development is 3.14. As the ramp above is a helicoidal surface, a definite relationship exists between the height of the curve (corresponding to the incline of the stairway) and its diameter. For a clear form, the outer radius of the curved surface should have the normal line of flight (line A). The inner radius thus becomes correspondingly steeper. When the inner radius is given the normal stair incline, the outer radius of the curve becomes flat, and the form appears bent (line B).

Determining the Radius of a Curved Return—Case 1

e Given are the incline of the stairway and the relative positions of the risers of the first step and also one down, from a common landing. Both risers are in the same vertical plane. For the given incline, make a schematic illustration of the development for the radius of a curved return with a selected, easy-to-draw scale. The individual straight lines are extended beyond the established triangle. The rise AB (dotted line) of the first step up is centered on the axis MP and the displaced parallel until it touches the incline line in A' and B'. This is the front edge of the desired return. A parallel to CM from A' intersects the axis PM in M'. The dimension M'D is the desired radius of the return.

Determining the Radius of a Curved Return—Case 2

f When the risers of the first step up and down from a common landing do not lie in the same vertical plane, a smaller return radius is created. Its size is found as in **e**, above, from the angle of incline of the stairway and the schematic development.

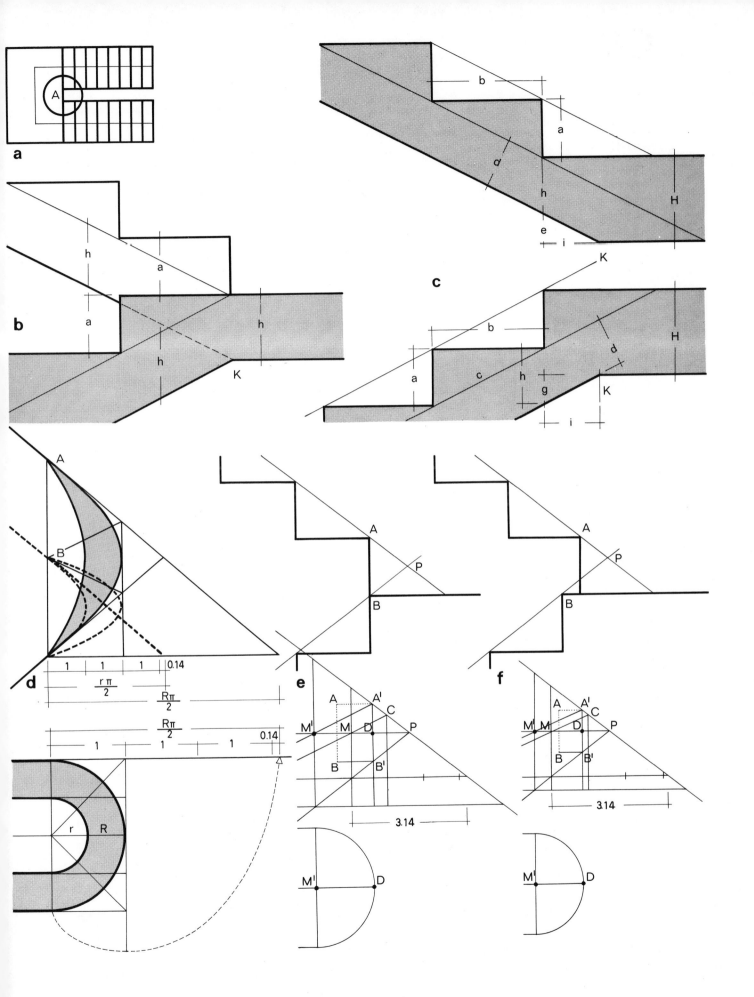

a

b

c

d

e

f

$\dfrac{r\,\pi}{2}$

$\dfrac{R\,\pi}{2}$

$\dfrac{R\,\pi}{2}$

1   1   1   0.14

1   1   1   0.14

3.14

3.14

r   R

C12 Arches

The arch appears in building projects for many purposes, in different sizes and in different types of construction. Its form and the execution thereof are decided by applicable statics, building technology, and aesthetics. Here the arch is treated only as a geometrical, curved form. Special forms can be developed from the arch without difficulty.

The Most Common Arch Forms

a_1 **The Norman arch,** a semicircle, is one of the oldest and most common arch forms. When it stands on a horizontal plane, it appears compressed, and not exactly a semicircle.

a_2 **The raised Norman arch** appears in elevation as a true semicircle when a good choice of height is made. (Here it is somewhat exaggerated.)

a_3 **Line of force arch (narrow).** The modern arch forms are derived from the lines of force in the arch as determined by statics.

a_4 **Line of force arch (wide).** The line of force can also be relatively flat. It depends upon the specific building problem.

The Parabola

b With a given span and height, the parabola is constructed by first dividing its height and one-half of its span into several equal parts (here, eight). From the center of the crown, draw a construction line to all division points on the lateral height line. Where construction line 1 intersects the perpendicular from point 1, on the base line, lies a point on the parabola, etc.

Tangents to a Parabola at a Selected Point

The height h from the selected point A to the crown S of the parabola is transferred perpendicular above S toward A'. The line A'A is the desired tangent.

Segments to Determine a Selected Arch Form

c In order to determine a selected arch by dimension, it is divided into a number of circle segments, which make up its form. Start in the center of the arch and, working to the left and right, link the necessary number of segments. Although in the drawing the transition points of the individual segments may not be noticeable to the eye, the arch form must still be confirmed and smoothed out where necessary.

Adapting an Arch Form to the Terrain

d Of three circular arches, the one on the right stands on rising terrain, and the top of the bridge also follows this incline. If the third arch is drawn as a circle, it will be partially sunk in the terrain, and the top of the bridge will be raised above its crown. However, the arch form is correct only if the arch follows the incline as in d_1.

Norman Arches

e A Norman arch in elevation, plan, and section. In this arch form, it must be considered that under certain circumstances a door or window cannot be opened completely because its edge will not clear the archivolt. Just how far a casement window can be opened without interference by the archivolt is indicated in plan by a broken line. The plan shows a section outline of the plane in which point A revolves when a window or door is opened. This outline appears as a hyperbola (corresponding to C3 **c**). It illustrates where the opened window or door touches the circular jamb. Actually, however, another point near A makes contact with the arch first. (The opening sash constitutes a revolving body which intersects the hollow cone-shaped opening.)

f **Norman arches in stone.** Sizes of the individual stones are determined and fixed in the elevation of the arches. From the elevation, the cut of each of the stones is developed. The stones are then numbered for laying on the job site.

g **A Norman arch with segment arches in its archivolt.** There is a solution that enables the sash to open without interference by the archivolt. The interior face of the archivolt is formed flat up to the crown of the highest point of the arch. The upper part of the archivolt is detailed as a series of segment arches. Between the Norman arch and the upper segment arch, there is a curved surface made up of straight lines (dot-dash lines) between both arches. It is an even surface; that is, a surface created with a straight line by the joining of two lines (here a circular arch and a segment arch). (The surface is not the conical one of the oblique circular cone, which is the result of the Norman arch and the circle with the radius of the segment arch, indicated by dots in the cross section.)

The cross section between the lateral surface of the archivolt and the normal surface is determined by means of perpendicular assisting planes parallel to the visible plane. In the example, the cutting lines of the assisting planes are Norman arches. The central point of these circles is determined by the fact that the middle axis between arch and segment arch and an arbitrary straight line corresponding to the ruled surface are subdivided into the selected intervals of the assisting planes in the ground plan (in this case, four equal parts). The dividing points are connected by straight lines. The perpendiculars from the bisecting point of these straight lines will give the central point for the cutting circles of the assisting planes on the vertical axis of the arch.

Ruled Surfaces

Ruled surfaces are formed by connecting straight lines between two lines whose points have a specific relationship to each other. These two lines can be straight (e.g., see C16) or curved (as in **g**, above, etc.).

h_1 **A ruled surface between two circles** corresponding to **g**, above.

h_2 **A ruled surface between a circle and a straight line.**

h_3 **An oblique cone.** The straight lines between both circles are, in this case, surface lines or elements of the cone.

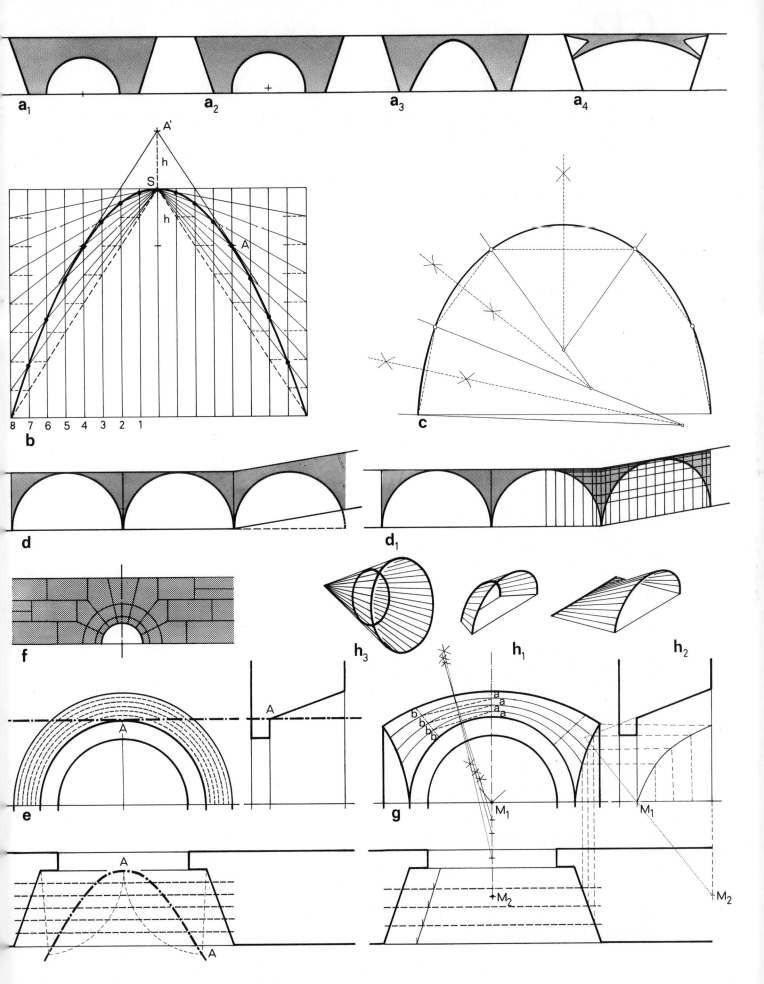

a_1 a_2 a_3 a_4

b

c

d d_1

f

h_3 h_1 h_2

e g

C13 Vaults

Barrel Vaults

The simplest form of vault is one-half of a circular cylinder, the so-called barrel vault. Openings or other penetrations in its form are intersections of the cylinder, the construction of which corresponds to C1 and C2.

Semicircular Opening in a Barrel Vault

a As its opening, a small semicircular vault intersects a larger semicircular vault. In plan the line of intersection is constructed according to C1.

A Cone-shaped Opening in a Barrel Vault

b An opening consisting of a cone with vertical walls intersects a semicircular barrel vault. The intersection is constructed by surface lines on the surface of the cone and their piercing points on the vault.
Generally, in the construction, forming for the larger vault (usually a barrel vault) is completely built, and the piercing bodies are then formed separately and attached (when not built in place).

The Roman Cross Vault

c When two circular cylinders of the same size possess common planes of intersection perpendicular to their axes (see C1 **c**), their common intersection lines are ellipses. In this case, the ellipses cross each other at 90° angles and in plan appear as diagonals of a square. In the forming, one vault is completed and the other is built on top of it.

Oblique Vaults (Arches)

d In a vertical wall, the front opening of a vault appears as a circle. In plan, however, the axis of the vault runs oblique to the wall. The arch form perpendicular to the vault axis is an ellipse. A section view showing the profile of the ellipse is revolved into the horizontal plane. Its development in the direction of its length reveals a surface bordered by two parallel curves. When the oblique arch is executed in stone, complicated joints are created on the interior curved surface (see development). Here the arch is executed with the depth of one stone. As soon as it gets deeper and more stone courses are required, a vault is created in which each stone has a different shape. The planning of oblique vaults and arches requires special care in both designing and detailing all materials.

Lines of Force in Oblique Arches

d₁ In oblique arches, when only a wall opening is involved, the execution remains simple. When it is a vault, the extent of existing forces must be considered, relative to the top illustration. However, in each simple brick vault, the forces run perpendicular to the vault axis, as in the lower illustration, which shows that the vault has no support.

Oblique Circular Openings

e The openings at both ends of the vault appear as ellipses, the sizes of which depend on the inclines of the embankment through which the vault runs. The form of the opening is constructed by the use of surface lines along the cylinder which intersects the embankment (broken lines = construction lines). Illustration in plan, elevation, and section.

e₁ Pictorial illustration of the cylinder and differently inclined intersecting planes.

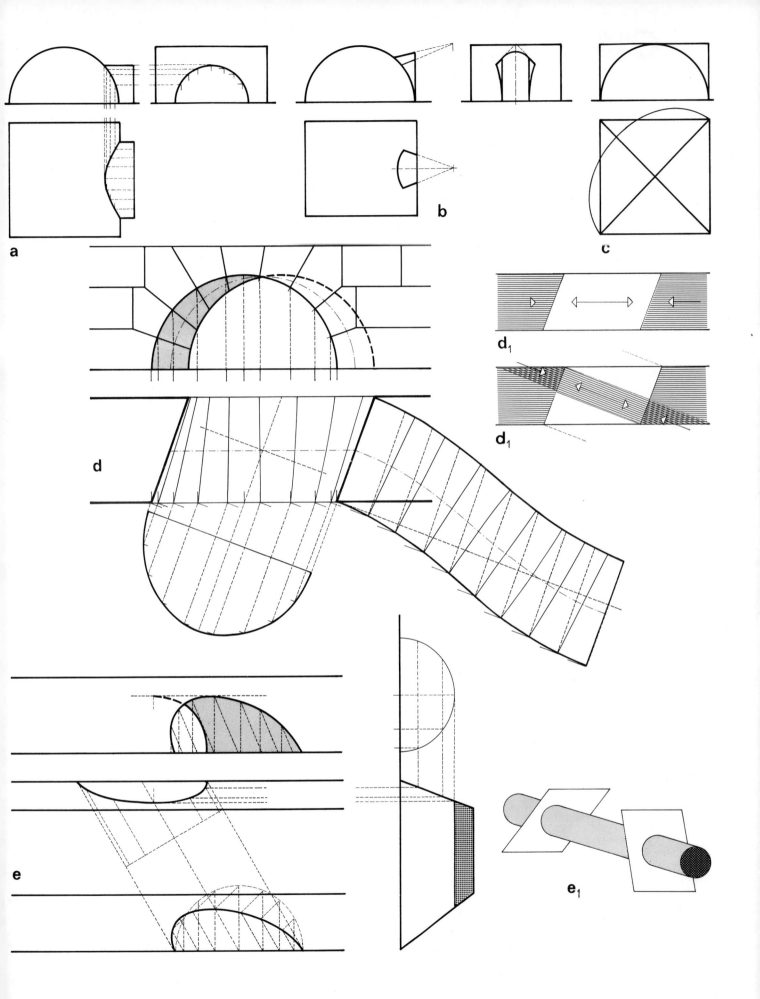

a

b

c

d

d_1

d_1

e

e_1

105

C14 Vaults over a Square Plan

a Oblique drawing of a semicircular barrel vault over a square plan, the simplest vault form.

b If this vault is cut through diagonally, two forms are created: the end section with the semicircular arch, and the side section.

c The Roman cross vault consists of four end sections over a square plan. Geometrically, it is the intersection of two cylinders of the same size. The lines of intersection make two ellipses (see C1 **c**).

d The cloister vault consists of four side sections (as illustrated). From the standpoint of statics, it is better than the cross vault. However, this form creates difficulty in the installation of windows and, probably for this reason, never attained the success of the cross vault.

Forming the Cross Vault

e A Roman cross vault in elevation and plan. When the crowns of the end sections lie horizontal, the diagonal ribs have the form of an ellipse (broken line, in plan). In terms of statics, this is not good. For this reason, as early as the thirteenth century, the cross vault in larger buildings was often modified by raising the crowns of the end sections (dot-dash line). Point A on the Roman arch has the height h in elevation. Directly above, point A' on the diagonal rib has the dimension h + b, which is determined by the incline of the vault. In order to determine the true size of the diagonal rib in plan, the height dimensions are revolved 90°.

In the building process, two end sections are formed opposite each other, then the other two. The increase in height, b, should not be too great, as the ridges between end sections near the top of the incline cannot be formed with exactness.

Spherical Vaults with Circular Openings

f The sphere has the same form in plan and elevation. The piercing points of the openings in the sphere are constructed by surface lines along the opening. The location of these points are determined in plan and elevation (or section). For the surface lines along the circular cylinder which pierce the sphere (broken lines), three points are always constructed. Point 1 lies at the transition from the straight lines of the side walls. Point 2 lies at any point on the cylinder, and point 3 lies at the crown. Draw vertical auxiliary planes through the surface lines which cut circular cross sections in the sphere, appearing in true size in the side elevation only. Because the auxiliary plane 3 always goes through the midpoint of the sphere, it will have the diameter of the sphere; the other diameters will be smaller. The piercing points for 1, 2, and 3 are established in the side elevation from the intersections of the surface lines with the circular sections. From here they are transferred to the revolved side elevation (for the diagonally piercing cylinders) and to the plan.

Barrel Vaults with Semicircular Openings in Stone

g Barrel vault, as in C13 **a.** Illustrated are plan (reflected)

and front and side elevations. A layout of the bond for execution in stone is desired. The barrel vault is constructed as in C13 **a.**

The layout of the stone is developed in the elevation. The course heights for the large and the small vaults must always be determined in section first. Corresponding to these course heights, the stone is then drawn to show the transition from the small to the large cylinder. In the process, care must be taken to insure a good stone bond. The joints of these stones in the barrel vault are straight in elevation; in plan, an ellipse (broken line), whose half-axis corresponds to the radius of the vault. The other half-axis is determined from the elevation at the intersection of the plane in which the joint lies, together with the crown line of the vault.

h Oblique drawing of the stone H. Work with stone profiles has substantially added to the development of descriptive geometry and technical drawing since the seventeenth century. Occasionally, today, stone profiles must still be drawn and cut. To illustrate complicated pieces, it is recommended that they be shown in a pictorial view. It is necessary to draw the entire block as a prism (here plan and front and side elevations) from which the stone must be cut. The dimensions can be laid off from its edges, as indicated, in a pictorial drawing—isometric or other.

a

b

c

d

e

f

g

h

C15 Vault Forms

Cross Vaults over a Rectangular Plan

A cross vault over a rectangular plan is an intersection of two cylinders of unequal size and therefore creates a number of problems in construction and form which do not occur with cross vaults over a square plan. The intersection curves are determined as in C1 **a** or C1 **f**. Further developments of the cross vault over a rectangular plan, beginning with an increase in height of the ridge (as in C14 **e**), ultimately lead to the Gothic arch.

Vault Axes of Equal Height

a The midpoints of the circles lie at the same height in elevation. When, over a rectangular plan, the large circle is executed as a barrel vault and the small ones are joined as two ascending cylinders, curved lines of intersection in two directions are created (similar to C1 **a**). There is practically no cross vault.

b The midpoints of the circles lie at the same height. When, over a rectangular plan, the small circle in the vault is carried through as a barrel vault and the large circle joined thereon as two descending cylinders, a cross vault is created whose ribs, in two directions, are irregular curves of intersection (see also C1 **f**).

Vault Crowns at the Same Height

c Both vault crowns are horizontal. The large visible arch is a circle, the small one an ellipse. The large circle is carried through as a barrel vault; the smaller vault, an elliptical cylinder, is joined thereon. This solution is unsatisfactory because the elliptical vault form does not harmonize with the circular vault form.

d Both vault crowns are horizontal. Both visible arches in elevation are circles and are executed as barrel vaults. The unequal heights of the midpoints of the semicircles cause the intersection line between the large and the small cylinder to start at some distance from each corner (see dark area of illustration).

Ascending Vaults

e Cross vaults with semipointed arches. The diagonal ribs lie in one plane (straight projection in plan). The large circle in elevation is carried through in two directions as an ascending barrel vault. The vaults formed from the small circle are executed as ruled surfaces between the diagonal ribs (see C12 h_1 and h_2). (If the vaults were circular cylinders, the ribs would not lie in one plane; instead, they would appear as curves in plan, as in **d**, above.)

f Cross vaults of pointed arches. Arches and ribs developed in elevation as pointed arches produce the most uniform vault over rectangular plans and all other areas. The purely geometrical considerations can be historically followed in the transition of the Norman to the Gothic style.

Spherical Vaults, Domes

The sphere encloses the greatest amount of space with the least amount of surface. For this reason it was of special meaning (in either its simple or combined forms) as vaults. This is also true in contemporary construction.

g Spherical vault over a square prism. The sides of the prism cut the sphere into circles. Each section of a sphere is a circle.

h Combined spherical vaults. Nothing more than a hemispherical vault is placed on top of the vault form in **g**, above. This is a form which appears frequently in architectural history.

i Spherical vaults over a spherical triangle. The modern solution of a spherical vault (example: Kresge Memorial, Boston, by Eero Saarinen).

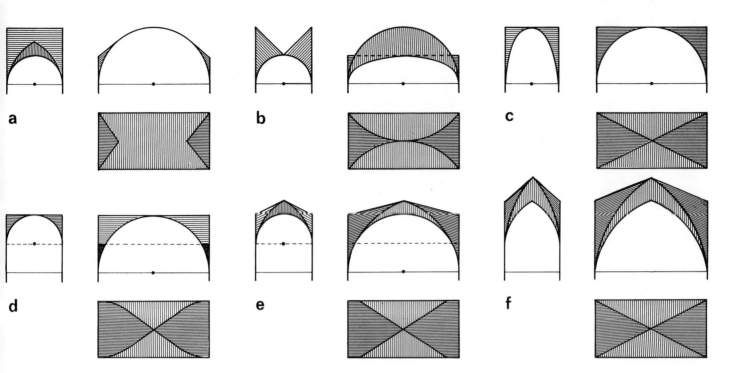

a

b

c

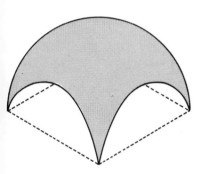

d

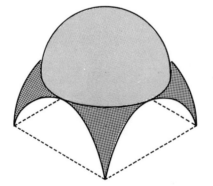

e

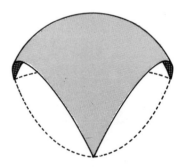

f

g

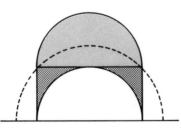

h

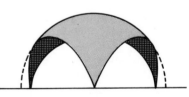

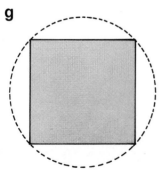

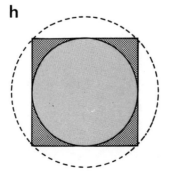

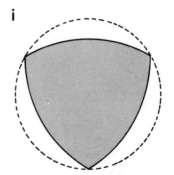

C16 Contemporary Vault Forms

To span a roof over large spaces requires vaults which cannot be built with traditional building methods. Modern cranes, methods of forming, and other recently developed construction principles make new solutions possible. The details of construction are decided primarily by the structural engineer. Together with him, the architect further develops the selected form to its execution. The drawing of such buildings requires very exacting work and a good deal of training in space relationships. Use of the foregoing constructions will be found especially in detailing connections, corners, and points of intersection.

Here only the most important of the contemporary forms is shown: the hyperbolic parabola. This is a double-curved surface between two sets of lines inclined to each other in space, which in a certain projection (here, in plan) appear as parallels. They have the same angle of incline, but in opposite directions. Corresponding points on the two lines are connected with straight lines and thus determine the surface.

Hyperbolic Parabola

a Schematic drawing showing the order of the straight lines between points 1 and 5 in plan and front and side elevations. The line in the center is the horizontal. To its left and right, the ascent (and corresponding descent) increases as the lines lie nearer the edges. The first and the last lines (here, 1 and 5) make up the outer edge of the surface.

b Hyperbolic parabola over a square plan divided into 14 equal parts. The purely geometrical form corresponding to the angle of inclination of two sides is drawn in plan and in both front and side elevations. When this scheme is adapted to an actual building project, construction dimensions, roofing, eave details, etc., should also be considered. For the construction of any detail point, start projections from the view in which the surface appears flat (here, in plan).

c An oblique view of the drawing in **b,** above, to illustrate the path of the straight lines of the roof surface.

d Plan of the corner with point A showing the construction size of the exterior beam. The run of the first three areas of the divided surface is drawn, corresponding to **b,** above, for the top and bottom of the roof. In order to determine the true size and angle, rotate the end beam parallel to the picture plane (broken line). If the outside side surface of the end beam is laid perpendicular to the horizontal plane, a break is created between the roof surface and the top of the end beam, reference A_1 and A_2. This is the simplest solution for the detailing of the end beam.

d₁ Front elevation of the corner with point A. The construction height of the end beam and its true angle are drawn with broken lines.

d₂ Side elevation of the corner with point A.

d₃ The front elevation of the end beam whose side surface is detailed perpendicular to the roof surface. This form is architecturally more pleasing than that with the end-beam sides perpendicular to the horizontal plane, but it is more difficult to construct.

e Pictorial view of the end beam in **d₁,** drawn at twice the scale.

110

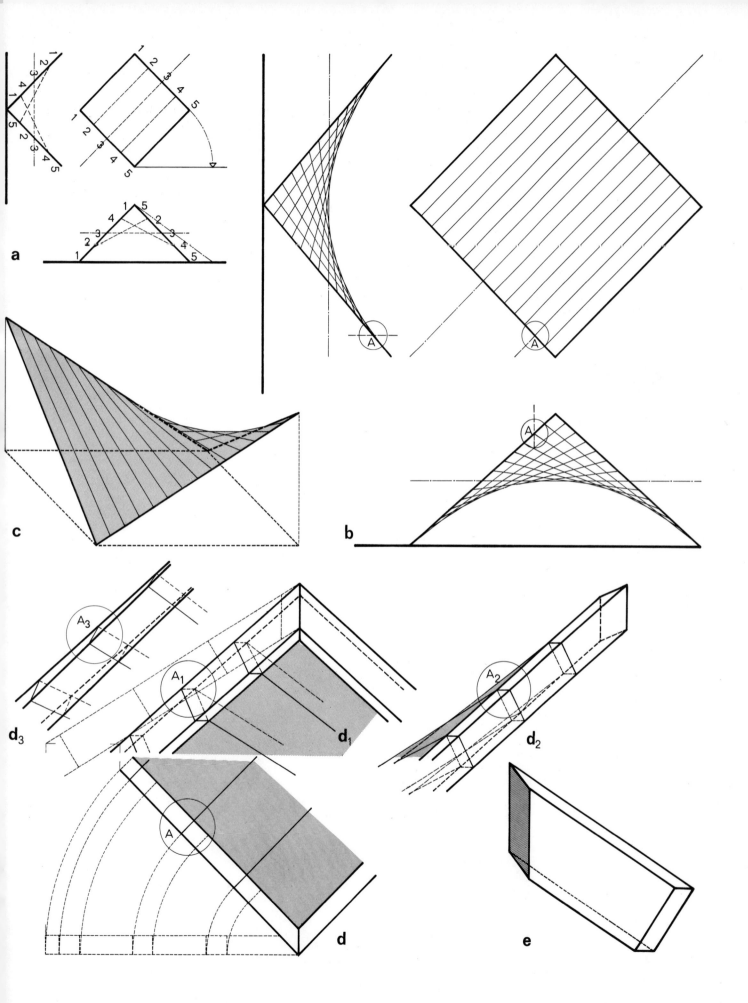

a

b

c

d_3

A_3

A_1

d_1

A_2

d_2

A

d

e

111

Index